# Face-to-Face with Doug Schoon Volume I

## Science and facts about nails/nail products for the educationally inclined.

Revised Volume 1 contains fact-based answers to questions from actual nail professionals in addition to newly clarified nail anatomy.

Based on
"Face to Face with Doug Schoon", Episodes 1-50.

ISBN 978-0-9979186-0-1
Library of Congress Control Number: 2016916821

Adapted from the scripts of:

"Face-to-Face with Doug Schoon"

Episodes 1-50

# Volume 1

# Contents

# Foreword

All nail professionals are not created equal, much in the same way that no two school experiences are alike, and education is a key component in being safe, smart, and successful. With varying requirements from state to state and country to country, the responsibility of knowing current nail trends, science, and healthcare falls on the nail professional. Unfortunately not even the clientele enjoying nail services are aware of the differences in levels of education and service which can result in infection, injury, or death due to ignorance, laziness, and greed.

As a nail professional myself, I have fallen in love with science-based education which means proven and factual information, constantly seeking out new and changing ways of maintaining the health and integrity of the clients hands, feet, and nails. This ranges from knowing and understanding anatomy along with proper nail terminology to the chemistry and accurate use of products. My favorite source of science since I met him over fifteen years ago has been Doug Schoon. In the salon as a working nail professional and as a regular blogger for NAILS Magazine, I am constantly using Doug's information to stay informed, refresh my knowledge, and check facts before answering questions or in reference to my writing.

This book is an amazing contribution to the nail industry and should be read by all whom consider themselves to be educated professionals. He has taken some of the most asked questions in the industry and answered them personally in a Face to Face episode, then gone on to compile them along with detailed answers in these pages. Even as the FingerNailFixer®, I found myself learning while reading this book. Just goes to show that no matter who you think might have a chance of knowing it all, there's always more to learn because our industry is constantly evolving and the products improving while becoming more technical and advanced.

Doug is a smart, talented scientist with a passion for seeing nail professionals succeed and find the respect they deserve for a craft they have mastered. You can almost feel how much he wants to help you personally as you read his answers throughout this book, or click on the links to view a Face to Face episode with even more information presented by Doug himself! The great thing about the information in these pages is that it is universally true making it absolute #nailtruth no matter where you are in the world. This means there is no reason for any of us not to own this book and proudly recommend it to everyone that does nails with hopes that by sharing accurate information, we can slowly advance the entire industry one nail fact at a time!

Holly L Schippers
FingerNailFixer®

# Liquid/Powder Nail Coatings

## Section 1

Those with active subscriptions to "Face-to-Face with Doug Schoon" Internet video series can click on the Episode number and questions below and watch Doug Schoon reply (E-readers only).

To get your subscription visit
www.FacetoFacewithDougSchoon.com

**EPISODE: QUESTION**

### 7:1 How do nail dehydrators improve adhesion of L&P nail coatings to the natural nail?

L&P nail coatings must adhere to the topmost surface of the nail plate. Excessive moisture and oils on the surface can block adhesion by preventing the molecules of the monomer liquid from physically and/or chemically bonding with the molecules that make up the surface of the nail plate. In a similar manner, butter prevents eggs from sticking to the frying pan; this is where adhesion occurs, between two surfaces. Adhesion happens when two very different surface molecules meet up and their molecules bond together in large numbers.

To "dehydrate" means to remove water from the surface of the nail plate. Removing moisture is the exact same thing, just said differently. This is because moisture is water and water is moisture. Nail dehydrators are solvents that can dissolve small amounts of moisture and cause the moisture to evaporate from just the upper most surface of the nail plate. Nail dehydrators will temporarily dehydrate the upper surface. Within a short time, moisture will begin to migrate back to the nail's upper surface, which will reverse the dehydration process. This will continue until the surface is rehydrated to normal levels, which could take up to 30 minutes or more, depending on the moisture content of the nail and the Relative Humidity (RH) of the room.

The nail won't remain in a dehydrated state for very long, so nail coatings should be applied shortly after the dehydration step is completed. After applying the nail dehydrator, **DO NOT** physically touch the nail with your fingers since this will re-deposit moisture and oils back on the plate's surface and cause recontamination. If moisture touches the nail plate, this will immediately reverse any surface dehydration.

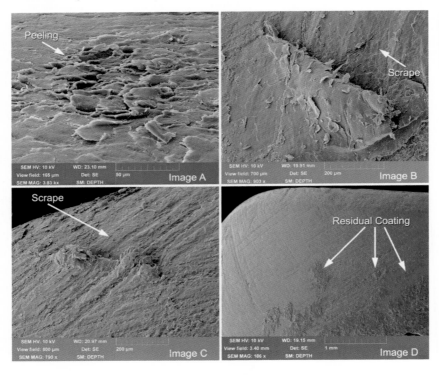

Don't blow on the nail to speed up drying, this just contaminates the nail plate with moisture from your breath. Finally, it is best to use nail dehydrators on clean nails and **NEVER** refill the same bottle with fresh product. Why? Nail dehydrators will also remove surface oils. That's not its function, since dehydration is the removal of "moisture". Even so, if the nail plate is not properly pre-cleaned to remove surface oils, residual oils can block adhesion. Hand washing using a clean and disinfected soft bristle nail brush is a great way to ensure these surface oils have been removed so that proper adhesion can develop. If these surface oils are not properly removed before using a brush-on nail dehydrator, they will be picked up and dissolved by the nail dehydrator, along with the moisture. When the brush is dipped back into the bottle, these oils are transferred into the bottle or other container. Over time, the nail oil concentration inside the container can increase. After a while, the oil concentration inside the container can become so high that each brush stoke of nail dehydrator re-deposits MORE nail oil onto the nail plate than is removed. When this occurs, adhesion to the nail plate can be compromised and lifting may result.

It's a myth that nail dehydration causes permanent white spots on the surface of the nail. Dehydration of the nail plate only occurs at the top most surface and is only temporary. Dehydrating the nail's surface does NOT cause permanent damage. Permanent damage is more properly attributed to physical trauma caused by scraping, prying or picking nail coatings from the nail plate as shown in images A-D.

**9:1 Some brands say to use primer wet, others say to wait till it dries. Many nail techs are confused about this and it is always up for debate. Who's right?**

Some primers can cause discoloration of the nail coating and possibly the natural nail as well, if not allowed to dry. This can also lead to tiny bubbles in the product. If you are using a technique that is NOT in accordance with manufacturer's instructions, these types of unintended consequences can be the result.

So, if you are applying a nail coating over wet primer and having discoloration issues, you should check to make sure you are correctly using the nail primer. Be sure to follow directions for use and heed all warnings and precautions provided by the manufacturer of the nail coating product of your choice.

**13:6 I bought a tool that allows me to pinch in the sidewalls of the artificial nail before it cures to get a deeper C-curve. Is this ok, or can pinching like this cause problems down the road?**

Pinching is a nail competition technique that some use every day, but I don't recommend doing this. Pinching in the side walls before the product cures will force the center of the nail coating to pull the nail plate upward. When the product cures, this locks the nail plate into this new position; creating a constant upward tugging on the nail bed, pulling the nail plate away from the bed.

This tugging can place excessive tension on the nail bed tissue and result in causing the nail plate to separate from the nail bed tissue, a condition called onycholysis (on-EE-ko-LY-sis). If you are using this type of technique and your clients are experiencing nail plate separation from the nail bed; you should immediately suspect this technique is the cause and discontinue pinching the sidewalls. Also, if the client's nail beds become sore or sensitive to touch you should suspect that this constant tugging is the reason. A little pinching may be ok, but if your clients nail plate develops any of these symptoms, that means you are probably pinching too much. Use caution and protect the nail!

**18:4 I have always been made to believe that acid primers are not advisable to use as it destroys the natural nail by slowly eating it away. Recently I heard that acid primers are the only way of "opening" up the layers of the nail to create better adhesion of the acrylic to the natural nail and those acid free primer/bonders are just a sticky substance that will only help to adhere to products to the very top layer of the natural nail?**

You were told incorrectly. Try this experiment; soak a piece of nail clipping in any nail primer and you will find that even after months or years of complete immersion, these products will NOT eat the nail. This silly myth was started by some irresponsible UV gel companies in Europe during the late 90's solely to frighten nail techs. They wanted to trick nail technicians into thinking that two-part liquid monomer and polymer powder systems were harmful to the nail. Why, they only sold UV gel products, so they pretended UV gels were safer and healthier, which is false and misleading. All professional nail coatings can be used safely and none should damage the natural nail when properly applied, maintained and removed.

The primers "eat the nail" myth and other false rumors like this were spread just so these companies could unfairly gain a competitive advantage over the competition, companies selling liquid monomer and powdered polymer systems. This is called "fear-based marketing" and sadly such scare tactics can work when nail professionals don't have correct information. Here is the correct information:

Artificial nail primers work in one of two ways;

1. The traditional methacrylic acid based primers act like double sided sticky tape, but they aren't sticky. Instead, the primer molecules have two arms or branches. One branch is strongly attracted to the nail plate while the other branch chemically reacts to become part of the enhancement. This anchors the enhancement to the plate and prevents lifting. Methacrylic acid primers aren't used that much anymore because they are very corrosive to skin and may cause serious burns when accidental exposure occurs.

2. Newer technology primers don't use methacrylic acid, are not corrosive and provide improved adhesion. Some of the new primers also behave like double sided sticky tape as described above, while other types actually form strong chemical bonds directly to the keratin protein to provide enhancement with superior adhesion.

Lastly, no primer can "open up the layers" of the nail plate and ALL professional nail primers work only on the surface of the nail plate. How do you decide which primer to use? I recommend that you use the primer that was designed for use with the system that you choose to use.

**24:2 Can you give me an explanation of MMA and why it causes nail damage? I have had a few clients referred to me with severely damaged nail plates and nail beds. Nothing sticks to their nails after 2 years of having this applied to them. I need a simple explanation for them.**

MMA stands for methyl methacrylate. The first thing to understand is that there is a very big difference between MMA "monomer" and MMA "polymer". When MMA is polymerized into long chains, it is no longer a monomer, it becomes a polymer. Monomers are individual molecules, while polymers are very long chains of monomers. MMA can typically form polymer chains that are more than 100,000 monomers long. This explains why polymers have completely different properties and are not the same as the monomers. They just have similar sounding names; such as polyMMA or poly methyl methacrylate. The "poly" indicates that the substance polymer is NOT the same as MMA monomer.

MMA was first turned into a polymer in 1877, but didn't become widely used until 1933 when it was sold under the brand name "Plexiglas". During World War 2 it was used to make submarine periscopes and aircraft windshields because it was much more durable than standard glass. Now it is used to make everything from automobile tail-lights, kitchen appliances and mixing utensils for cooking, lenses for eye glasses, home windows, skylights, signs and displays, bath tubs, LCD screens, furniture and many other everyday products.

MMA is also polymerized along with other monomer to make customized artificial nail powders used in liquid and powder systems. It is considered safe and appropriate to use for this purpose. However, I can't say the same for MMA "monomer". The use of MMA monomer in artificial nail products has been an on-going issue for more than 25 years. Many have worked to stop the improper use of methyl methacrylate monomer as an artificial nail coating, however MMA is still widely used. Why? The main reason is cost; nail products containing MMA monomer sell for up to 75% less than the professional products which don't contain MMA monomer. Many salons use this low cost monomer to undercut the service prices of other salons in their area. This helps explains why the use of MMA monomer has become more of an emotional issue than one that is fact-based. As a result of this unfair competition, many of the reasons given to avoid MMA are NOT based on factual information. Instead, many act on anger and frustration. Some nail professionals lashed out and began to spreading misinformation about MMA monomer, largely because they themselves lacked the correct information. Some erroneously claimed MMA monomer causes cancer, birth defects or was highly toxic; all of which are untrue.

MMA monomer is used by doctors around the world and is considered the best and most widely used bone cement in the world. Which means it is implanted into the body to mend badly broken bones. It can't be all that bad when it is regularly implanted into the body and for more than 40 years. But even though MMA is very safe and useful bone cement, it's a lousy monomer ingredient for artificial nail coating products.

These are the real reasons MMA monomer should NOT be used as an ingredient in artificial nail liquids:

A. MMA monomer products do not adhere well to the natural nail unless the nail plate is aggressively filed, which many call "roughing up" the nail plate. The only way to make this monomer adhere well is by shredding the surface of the natural nail. Anything will adhere better to the nail plate when it's shredded, but the practice is harmful to the client's nails. This thins and weakens the natural nail plate, setting clients up for future problems.

For example, this can lead to separation of the plate from the nail bed or onycholysis, increased nail plate cracking/breaking and increased potential for future lifting issues. As the saying goes, "You can't build a strong house on a weak foundation." Aggressively filing and overly thinning the nail plate creates a weak foundation.

B.  MMA artificial nails are extremely difficult to remove.

That is because MMA is highly impervious to acetone and other nail coating removal solvents. MMA nail coatings often become brittle and discolor quickly. They must be removed every three or four months. This increases the risk of nail damage, especially when it is considered that MMA nails are often removed by prying the enhancement from nail plates. Prying or forcing any nail coating from the nail plate causes pitting and other surface damage, to create deep pits in the surface further weakens the natural nail plate.

C.  MMA artificial nails are extremely rigid and very difficult to break.

When they are accidentally jammed or caught, the overly thinned natural nail plate often breaks before the MMA enhancement. This can lead to serious nail plate cracks which expose the bed and can lead to infections. I've designed some of the most successful nail enhancement products ever sold. One of the keys to their success is that IF they are caught or jammed the enhancement would break BEFORE the nail plate broke.

These are the real reasons why MMA monomer should not be used in artificial nail coating products. MMA containing nail coating products are harmful to the natural nail no matter how they are applied. Regulations alone have been very ineffective in controlling this problem. Regulations are only effective if someone actually shuts down the importers and suppliers and that has never been done, to my knowledge. Instead, all the attention and blame was placed on salons and technicians using these products. In the meantime, the MMA sellers rack up huge profits, selling MMA through the gray markets or underground channels. Some openly sell on the Internet and little is done to stop them. Unless stiff fines and serious consequences are enforced on importers and suppliers, MMA sales will continue. But in my view, TOO much focus is placed on creating unenforceable regulations and trying to force nail technicians into not to using MMA. Instead, we should be educating nail professionals about 'why' MMA monomer shouldn't be used. Please do not create irrational fear by claiming MMA nails causes cancer or birth defects, they don't and there is no fact-based evidence to support these claims. Its fear-based nonsense designed to frighten... not to inform. There is a much bigger problem here that many aren't considering.

Nail professionals who use MMA monomer products are often uneducated about how to properly prepare the nail plate without damaging it. These nail technicians often poorly control their product application which can cause allergic skin reactions and they often use damaging removal techniques. Even if these nail technicians changed to non-MMA products, they still would use incorrect and damaging techniques. These technicians need proper information and better education, not a slap on the hand or a small fine. They are under educated about how to properly perform these services.

Consumers don't know the difference between MMA, EMA, BMA or RMA and they DON'T really care. In the consumer's mind, they're all artificial nails and clients often associate MMA misinformation with all artificial nail products. The untrue myths just needlessly frighten clients and harm the entire professional nail industry in the process. No type of artificial nail product causes cancer or birth defects! There is no credible fact-based evidence that they do. The ingredients used to create these products are among the most widely studied ingredients on the planet, because they are used for so many different purposes. Please teach clients about the disadvantages of wearing MMA enhancements and don't repeat scary stories and myths. The client needs to understand why they should avoid patronizing salons that use MMA products and how to tell the difference.

Remember, an educated client is the best inspector and the best defense against salons that use MMA monomer. Teach your clients well so they know why MMA should be avoided. Explain that artificial nail coatings, when properly applied should NOT cause the problems I just described. Explain these potential problems are easily avoided by using high quality professional products and proper application and removal techniques. Clients should never feel pain, have skin redness or irritation or suffer nail damage as a result of any nail service. This can happen when any type of artificial nail coating is used improperly, but these problems are easy to avoid when the products are used correctly.

**29:1 I was wondering if you could settle an argument between me and another tech. Should nail technicians mix different brands of monomer and powder? Are there any risks other than the potential for service breakdown?**

When the incorrect nail powder is used with a monomer liquid, service breakdown can become a much bigger issue. Even so, there are more important problems which can develop when the incorrect powder is used. Under a microscope it's easy to see these powders are actually large numbers of tiny solid polymer spheres that are coated on the outside with various ingredients. Mixing them with monomer liquid causes a chemical reaction that creates a polymer coating with great durability. The monomer liquid is more important to the final properties of the nail coating, but the polymer powder is also extremely important. I'd estimate that 70% of the properties come from the liquid monomer and 30% from the polymer powders. These powders are NOT interchangeable between different company brands and there is NO such thing as a Universal Powder that works with all brands of monomer liquids.

Interestingly, when it comes to the individual powder particles themselves it's important to understand:

a) What is inside the particle?

b) What the outer surface like?

c) What is attached to the particle's surface?

All three of these are important to the final enhancement. The inside of the particle determines the strength. These particles must be strong enough to resist cracks and keep them from spreading. That's a main function of each powder particle, to act as crack arrestors to stop tiny cracks from quickly spreading and joining to create larger cracks. Without these powder particles, cracks would easily join together to cause the enhancement to quickly break. When there are too few of these powder particles in the enhancements or coating, breakage is more likely to occur.

The surface of each powder particle is even more important. The particle's surface determines much of it workability and compatibility with the monomer liquid. In other words, the outer surface determines how easily the powder can be picked up to create a bead. It also determines how well the mixture will flow when it is brushed and if it will stay where it is placed. Also, the ease with which the surface will self-level and the final surface smoothness and shine are determined by the powder. All of those factors are largely controlled by how well the particle's surface interacts with the monomer liquid. If they don't interact well, many of these properties are diminished. Additives that adhere to the surfaces of these particles help prevent yellowing, improve brightness or ensure better coverage.

The most important of these additives is benzoyl peroxide, which is often shortened to "BPO". Benzoyl peroxide is the same acne fighting ingredient which millions of teenagers have applied to their faces over the last 60 years. In acne creams, BPO is used in up to a 10% concentration. In nail powders, the BPO concentration is usually between 1-2%. Interestingly, there is a VERY big difference between a nail powder containing 1% verses a nail powder containing 2% BPO. These may sound like a small difference, but this is a BIG difference. A powder with 2% BPO contains twice as much BPO as one with only 1%. While other ingredients found in the monomer liquid are responsible for controlling how fast the coating will cure, the amount of BPO in the powder determines how "completely" the liquid monomer will cure.

This is VERY important for nail professionals to understand. Too little BPO, the enhancement will under-cure. Too much BPO, the enhancement will over-cure. Over curing can lead to discoloration, especially yellowing. It can also cause brittleness, cracking, breaking, chipping and loss of adhesion or lifting. These are all classic signs of service breakdown. Of course no one wants these types of problems with their nails, however, "under" cure is an even more important issue that must be avoided. Under-cured nail coatings often have service breakdown and are more likely to stain and can be overly flexible or have increased cracking at the stress zones near the free-edge. Even more importantly, under cured nail coatings are much more likely to cause adverse skin reactions for clients and nail professionals. In fact, I believe under curing is one of the leading causes of skin irritation and allergies to nail products, in general and this includes UV cured nail coatings. This is because under cured enhancements contain excessive amounts of uncured ingredients.

In the case of these two part systems, under cured nail coatings contain excessive amounts of monomers and their fresh dusts and filings are also rich in monomer. Prolonged or repeated contact to monomer-rich dusts and filings may lead to skin overexposure- which is a leading cause of skin allergy to nail enhancements. When prolonged and/or repeated skin contact is avoided, allergic reactions become highly unlikely. This explains why it is important keep arms from laying on dusts, filings, or from repeatedly contacting the backs of the hands, arms, neck, etc. When properly cured, these nail coatings will not contain excessive amounts of monomer and are unlikely to cause adverse skin reactions.

There are two main ways to cause under-curing. The most common is to apply product beads that contain too much monomer liquid and not enough powder. The amount of powder that is picked up to form the bead determines the amount of BPO in that bead. Use too little powder and there will not be enough BPO for proper curing. What is the proper amount of powder for a bead? The right amount creates a medium consistency bead that holds its own shape; never use a bead that has a runny or wet consistency. Also, never brush pure monomer onto the enhancements; this injects excessive amounts of monomer into the enhancements, which leads to under-curing. If you use the incorrect powder, it likely doesn't contain the correct amount of BPO. What do I mean by the incorrect powder? I'm talking about a powder that was not "specifically designed" to be used with the monomer liquid used. It is important to note that a 1% BPO powder will under cure a liquid monomer designed for use with a 1.5% BPO powder.

Even a half percent difference in BPO concentration can lead to an under-cured enhancement, and that is especially risky during the first hour after creating the enhancement. That's when the enhancement contains the highest concentration of uncured monomer and the potential for developing skin over exposure is at its highest. That's why it is important to avoid prolonged and repeated exposure to fresh filings and dusts. That is why I am opposed to so-called "universal powders". What's that all about? Why would one company sell a nail powder to cure another company's monomer liquid? It doesn't make sense, unless they just want to sell powder to as many nail technicians as they can and don't really care if the enhancement properly cures. In my opinion, it is wrong for one company to tell nail professionals to misuse another company's products. These are two part systems that should be used as directed.

I advise all nail professionals to:

1.  Only use the powder that was specifically designed for the monomer liquid used.

2.  Always use a medium consistency bead, never wet or runny.

3.  Never use monomer alone, always mix it with the powder.

4.  Avoid prolonged and/or repeated skin contact with fresh filings or dusts.

5. Avoid skin contact with any uncured nail coating products, including liquid monomers and UV cured gels or UV gel manicure products.

Once a nail coating is properly cured, they'll be very unlikely to cause adverse skin reactions. So be wise and use them well.

### 29:2 What size brush do you recommend to use with liquid and powder systems?

Avoiding skin contact with monomer is important to prevent adverse skin reactions. When overly large brushes are used, skin contact becomes very difficult to avoid, especially on smaller nail plates. Also, it becomes much harder to keep from using too much monomer liquid. Why? The belly of the brush will hold too much monomer which is injected into the enhancement when pressed against the nail.

To avoid this, squeeze out any excess by wiping the belly against the dappen dish rim. Don't wipe out the excess monomer on a table towel. Laying arms on the towels can cause allergic skin reactions. With any nail product, I recommend #8 size or smaller brush. Some can use a #10 brush, without over exposing the skin but greater care and attention is needed to prevent using too much monomer. I don't recommend brushes larger than a #10. In my view, that's trouble waiting to happen.

### 39:3 Could you please give me a little information on pinching enhancements? There are so many conflicting opinions!

As mentioned previously, pinching the sidewalls inward forces the center of the enhancement to pull the nail plate upward. These upward forces are focused in the exact spot where the nail plate's attachment to the nail bed is at its weakest.

This practice can lead to separation of the nail plate from the nail bed (onycholysis). This may be considered an acceptable competition technique, because no one wears their competition nails for very long. The more thoroughly someone pinches the sidewalls, the greater the risk of onycholysis.

If you are pinching a little, onycholysis is less likely. If you pinch a lot, onycholysis becomes more likely. Therefore, if you see any signs of onycholysis at all, this suggests that you are pinching too much. Some client's nails are highly prone to onycholysis, older clients for example often have weaker attachments to the nail bed, so onycholysis occurs more easily. This is why I recommend that nail professionals use this technique with great caution. Carefully monitor the nail plate and bed for any signs of detachment. And nail professionals should discontinue pinching the sidewalls if any onycholysis occurs.

# UV Nail Coatings

## Section 2

### 3:3 Are UV gels better for nails than other types of enhancements?

All nail enhancement products are safe for the natural nail if properly applied, maintained and removed. No type of artificial nail is safer or better for the natural nail than another. If nail damage occurs due to wearing enhancements, it is usually from over-filing or other improper practices during product application or removal. To prevent this, nail professionals should work in a manner that protects the natural nail and properly use artificial nail products. It is a fear-based marketing myth that certain types of nail enhancements are safer than others. This myth is designed to needlessly frighten people. Don't be fooled by fear-based marketing tactics, get the facts. If you do, you will learn that all artificial nail systems, including UV gels, are based on acrylic ingredients and use acrylic chemistry to harden or cure. There are no exceptions to this rule!

### 5: Special Topic I have a few questions about heat spikes during gel services. What causes them? Do they cause any damage to the client's nail, nail bed, nerve endings, or in any way cause harm to the client? Tips on how to avoid heat spikes would also be appreciated.

An exotherm is a scientific term that means "to release heat". This is what occurs when nail coating products get hot during application. Both UV gels and L&P systems can become warm, even hot during application. Becoming warm isn't a problem and is considered normal for products that cure or polymerize to create a nail coating. But when the coating over heats, this can be painful for clients. Even so, nail coating exotherm (EK-so therm) can cause other problems besides a burning pain. This type of overheating can lead to nail bed damage and infections. It is important to understand why these issues occur, so that you can avoid them. Let's look at the most common reason clients feel excessive heat when these types of products cure.

UV gels and monomer liquids are both made using acrylic ingredients and chemistry and there are **NO** exceptions to this rule. Curing occurs as millions of tiny, invisible molecules begin to permanently join together to create many growing polymer chains. Each time two molecules react to join together, there is a release of a very tiny amount of heat. The heat release by one molecule joining a chain is FAR too small to detect. However, when a coating cures on a single nail plate, it contains many millions of molecules. Many millions of molecules joining together release millions of times more heat. Of course, this normally occurs on every nail plate and usually doesn't create any problems. However, excess heating can become painful and potentially damaging under some circumstances. This can occur with all types of artificial nail coatings and adhesives. When nail coatings are properly formulated, properly applied and properly cured the small amount of heat that is released usually goes unnoticed.

Some products are not properly formulated and may have a tendency to overheat, even when properly applied. This is unusual because reputable manufacturers run quality control tests to ensure the heating is controlled so that it won't become excessive. This is one of many reasons for only purchasing such products from reputable manufacturers. Nail product developers pay very close attention to this issue and design their products to slowly release heat during curing, rather than to suddenly release it as a heat spike.

Even normal levels of heat become much more noticeable if the nail bed is injured, e.g. from aggressive over filing. Why? The nail plate insulates the nail bed from heat, but if the nail plate is overly thinned by filing, it becomes a poor heat barrier and this allows heat to flow through the plate into the nail bed, in some cases to cause injury. Also, overly aggressive filing techniques can "friction burn" the nail bed making it super-sensitive to even small amounts of heat that would normally go unnoticed. For example, if rub my arm with my fingers five times, that doesn't harm it, but if I do that 500 times I'm likely to damage the surface of the skin. Or if I push down harder and rub 50 times, I can still friction burn my skin and the same is true when filing the nail plate.

Do not burn the nail bed! File gently and avoid coarse abrasives that thin the nail plate. The nail bed doesn't contain any heat detectors, but does contain pressure detectors. You can feel these detectors activate if you pressed down hard on the nail plate. That's why you can feel applied pressure to the nail bed. However, when the nail bed gets hot enough, this will trigger the pressure detectors to create painful burning sensations. Generally these detectors won't be triggered until the temperature of the nail bed exceeds 115°F or 46°C. When that occurs, the nerve ending under the nail plate can go off like a fire alarm in the brain. The brain sends a pain strong signal back to the nail bed to warn it of a potential danger. Friction burns can damage the nail bed and make it very sensitive and cause it to over react to even warm temperatures. What can cause a monomer liquid and powder formula to overheat? Using the wrong powder polymer with the liquid monomer can definitely cause these types of nail coating products to over heat. That is why it is important to only use polymer powders designed for the monomer liquid of your choice. "Fast setting" nail coatings actually release the same amount of heat as those with traditional set time, however they do so in a shorter time period. This heat may go unnoticed when released over two or three minutes, but this same amount of heat becomes very noticeable when released in one minute or less. This is especially true if the nail bed has been friction burned by overly aggressive filing techniques. Fast setting nail coating products aren't for everyone. They are best used in cold climates. That's because the room temperature plays a big role in determining how quickly these monomer liquid and polymer powder nail coatings will harden (polymerize). Fast set nail coatings are much more likely to overheat when used on warm days.

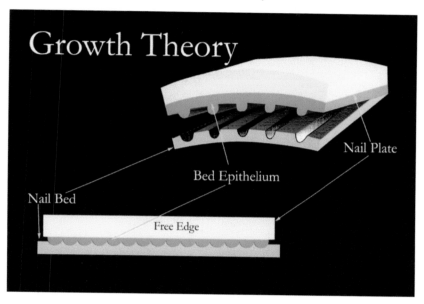

UV cured gel nail coatings can also create heat spikes, especially on friction burned nail beds. Heat spikes that occur during the cure of UV gels can be caused by using the incorrect UV nail lamp. For example, a UV gel nail coating designed to cure with traditional fluorescent style UV nail lamps will likely over heat when cured with a LED-style UV nail lamp. LED-style UV nail lamps produce more UV than traditional style nail lamps. That's why they cure nail coatings more quickly. When a UV gel nail coating designed to cure in 2 minutes under a fluorescent-style UV nail lamp is cured in 30 seconds with a LED-style UV nail lamp, all of the heat is released in one-quarter the time. This is what can create painful burning sensations and that may result in onycholysis (on-EE-ko-LY-sis), or separation of the nail plate from the nail bed. Onycholysis can lead to nail bed infections. Of course there are other reasons for onycholysis, which are discussed in other questions answered in this book. No matter which type of nail coating you use, the more thickly the nail coating product is applied, the more heat will be released. That's often why larger thumb plates feel warmer, compared to smaller nail plates.

To avoid these problems here are some general rules to follow:

- Avoid friction burns of the nail bed- Don't Burn the Bed!

- Don't over thin the nail plate, keep it healthy and intact.

- Use the correct polymer powder with monomer liquid of your choice.

- Avoid using fast setting L&P nail coatings when working in warm salons.

- Use the UV nail lamp recommend for use by the UV gel manufacturer.

- Avoid applying product too thickly, especially UV curing gels.

**8:1 I was taught that the inhibition layer on many UV coatings is there because the product cures from the nail plate up and it can't cure where oxygen is present, leaving a thin, and sticky, uncured inhibition layer. What about no cleanse gels? Why don't they have an inhibition layer?**

What you were told is mostly correct. UV nail products cure by UV exposure and during cure, UV energy is present at all layers inside the UV gel coating, so all layers are simultaneously curing throughout the entire nail. It's a myth that UV gels cure from the top down or bottom up. I've heard both and neither of these makes scientific sense.

The rest of the points you've made, I agree with. The sticky layer is due to oxygen in the air. Oxygen can block the curing process near the surface to keep the upper layers from properly curing. Because oxygen in the air blocks the curing process, this layer is properly called the "oxygen inhibition layer" or "inhibition layer", for short. This "sticky layer" is actually an improperly cured layer of UV gel. It has a gel-like consistency, because this layer is less than 50% cured. UV gel nail coatings harden when they are more than 50% cured. It's important to understand that "hardening" of the nail coating does not mean the coating is properly cured. This is important because this improperly cured UV gel, e.g. inhibition layer, has the potential to cause adverse skin reactions such as allergy or irritations. Skin contact should always be avoided with uncured or partially cured nail coating product, including dusts and roll off from filing. Avoid laying your arms in these dusts or roll-off or you may develop a skin sensitivity that could become permanent.

It is possible to formulate a UV gel that doesn't create an inhibition layer, but this creates big disadvantages. These formulas have a much higher tendency to overheat (exotherm) and burn the nail bed, which can lead to onycholysis and this can reduce the color stability of the coating and may cause it to become brittle over time. Also, the ingredients used to counteract the effects of oxygen can have a higher tendency to cause adverse skin reactions, so be especially cautious of prolonged or repeated contact with these uncured UV gels. I also recommend that you use caution when removing the sticky inhibition layer. Using cotton soaked pads to remove this layer can lead to skin contact with fingers and increase the potential for irritation or allergy. This is why I recommend using a plastic-back cotton pad or wearing disposable nitrile or vinyl gloves to help avoid skin contact with this uncured layer. Any type of uncured/improperly cured UV gel can cause adverse skin reactions if prolonged and/or repeated contact occurs. Remember, nail coatings that cure without an inhibition layer can have a higher tendency to cause skin sensitivity so avoid skin contact.

When properly applied and cured according to manufacturer's directions, all UV gel products can be used safely; however, this requires proper use and requires nail technicians to take care to avoid skin contact with the uncured UV gel, dust and filings. Failing to properly apply and cure UV nail coatings is a major reason for adverse skin reactions to such products. This is true for any UV curing nail product, since any of them can cause adverse skin reactions and there are no exceptions to this rule. Even so, it is easy to avoid these problems when nail coatings are proper applied and correctly cured. Skin sensitivities are generally due to improper handling or improper cure of UV gels.

**12:2 I use a freeze curing technique with the white UV gel. I'm removing the nail from the lamp after 30 seconds, exposing the white gel just long enough to solidify in at the free edge. Then I apply clear product to the rest of the nail and placing the hand back into the UV lamp for the remaining time. Does it interrupt the curing process when hands are removed from the UV lamps?**

If these are the instruction provided by the manufacturer of the UV gel, then perform this technique exactly as directed. If it is contrary to the instructions, then I recommend asking the manufacturer if this technique is acceptable. That's how to ensure there are no unintended or unforeseen consequences. The product manufacturer is responsible to tell you how to use their product correctly and safely.

From a chemical point of view, when the hands are removed from under the UV source, the curing process crawls to a very slow rate, but doesn't stop. Curing will continue at a very slow rate for weeks, even without additional UV exposure. That's why some UV gels become brittle over time, they eventually become over-cured. UV gels never really "completely" stop reacting and eventually can become brittle or begin to discolor because of these continuing reactions. Formulas that resist discoloration and brittleness are usually of higher quality, meaning they are well-formulated and carefully manufactured. A properly formulated UV gel enhancement resists becoming brittle or discolored for at least 16 weeks. That's how long it takes the nail plate to completely grow past the free edge. By then, all nail coating material has grown over the free-edge and been removed.

The good news is, when the hands are placed back under the UV source, the chemical reactions resume at the normal rate and the nail coating will eventually cure properly. Removing the hands temporarily does not negatively impact cure, just as long as you cure each thin layer of applied UV gel, as directed and for the proper length of time in the correct UV lamp.

**13:4 The area of my school in which I perform services is not as well-lit as I need. I want to purchase a table lamp, but I realized that some of the lamps are LED. Will an LED table lamp affect LED-cured gels? What type of close lighting would you suggest?**

I agree that you need good lighting and it sounds like the school should consider making an improvement in their lighting conditions, because poor lighting can be a safety hazard and create unnecessary risk. However, I need to explain that LED means "light emitting diode", which makes it a type of light bulb and NOT a type of light. It's a big myth that LED is the type of light coming out of the "bulb", but it's not! LEDs are just the bulb and many different colors can be emitted by LED's, in fact they can be made to emit every color of the rainbow, from red to violet. To clarify, I'm using the word "bulb" in the everyday sense, meaning something that actually emits light when enough electrical power is supplied, as in incandescent light bulb. Some refer to these as lamps or globes. For our purposes, we'll consider these to be the same as bulbs.

The mistake that some make is to assume a new kind of light is emitted and it is called "LED", and this LED stuff cures UV gels so you don't need to use UV. Wrong! This is a BIG mistake that many are making, including some doctors who are putting this misinformation on the Internet or misleading reporters when they are interviewed. The facts are the vast majority of LED's sold couldn't cure a single nail product. It's overly simplistic to assume that all LED's emit UV. Most of them do NOT.

Yes, a few types of LED's like those used in UV nail lamps, are specially designed so that they emit UV, but these are unique and special application within the wider world of LEDs. Even so, your question is a good one because many types of light bulbs also emit low levels of UV, including halogen lamps. You should be careful about what you use in the salon, if you use UV gels. If you aren't curing UV gels, then any type of table lamp that you chose would likely be fine.

For instance, even fluorescent office lighting emits low levels of UV, but these won't affect UV gel products, since the amount emitted is too low and the source is too far away from the nails. So your question becomes: Is there enough UV coming from a table lamp to affect UV gels and cause them to pre-maturely begin to cure the product? After all, these lamps are much closer than overhead lighting, so this becomes more likely. In some cases, the answer is yes, certain table lamps emit more UV than others. The most likely culprits are those which use so-called "true color" or "full spectrum" lamps/bulbs. These mimic natural sunlight and can be found either as fluorescent bulbs or as LED-style bulbs. These can emit significant amounts of UV, enough to begin to thicken your UV gel while it sits in the container. These types of lamps should be avoided in order to prevent "pre-mature cure".

Fortunately, it is pretty easy to determine which table lamps will pre-maturely cure the UV gels and which ones will not. To test a table lamp, all you need to do is coat a nail tip with the UV gel that you use in the salon and set it directly under your table lamp about 6 inches or 15 centimeters and leave it there for 15 minutes. If the UV gel appears to be unaffected, then the amount of UV coming from the table lamp is too low to cause an issue and the lamp is acceptable.

Repeat this same test with a true color or full spectrum lamp and the UV gel will very noticeably thicken or completely harden within the same span of time. That's because UV gels will harden once they reach the point where they are 50% cured. Even so, the UV gel doesn't need to be fully cured to indicate a potential problem with the table lamp. This is probably the best test you can perform to ensure your table lamp is not prematurely curing the product. Be sure to keep UV gel containers covered when not in use. Keep them away from the front side of your nail lamp, where UV exposure can occur. This is a common way that nail professionals prematurely cure their nail products, so beware of your product placement on the table. Premature curing can result in product that is difficult to apply and may quickly lift or develop other signs of service breakdown, e.g. discoloration. Keep these products away from sunlit windows to prevent premature curing on the brush, as well as in the container. Most of all remember, LED doesn't cure UV gels... only UV cures UV gels, including UV gel manicure products.

## 14:3 Why do some UV gel colors fade, while others don't?

Many colorants are affected by UV, since it can cause the colorant to undergo a chemical change that alters or fades its color. Some colors are more susceptible to UV than others. Those colors at the blue end of the color spectrum are generally easier to fade than those on the red end of the spectrum. Some colorants turn yellow with enough exposure to natural sunlight, since it contains UV energy. The reason some colors change and others don't depends on their chemical structure. Colors that have a chemical structure that is more resistant to UV are less likely to change.

How does UV cause the color to fade or shift? Like visible light, UV is energy. That's why its correct name is ultraviolet energy, and NOT ultraviolet light. Why not "light"? Light is energy we can see; if we can't see it, then it is not light. We can't see UV so it's not correct to call it "light". UV is pure energy! When UV collides with certain chemical bonds, this energy can snip them much like a scissor cuts a thread. When this happens, the color begins to fade or shift, because the chemical structure of the colorant ingredient is slowly changing. The more of these chemical bonds that break, the greater the change will be. Since these bonds aren't able to reconnect, the change is permanent and color is permanently altered. This is why newspaper slowly turns turn yellow when exposed to sunlight or why clothing slowly fades. It is also why cosmetic colorants in general fade and shift in color. This explains why it is important not to store your products in direct sunlight and why it is helpful to protect your nails from excessive sunlight exposure when outdoors.

**20:4 I had a client who was a very bad nail biter for years, she is also a nurse who has extremely damaged nails with deep grooves that don't appear to be infected. She asked me to help by giving her UV gels to help her stop biting. I thought this was a great idea since her nails were so damaged that she could be a health hazard at her job. Correct me if I am wrong, but isn't there a less likely a chance of bacteria growing on top of the enhancement particularly UV gel because it is not as porous as other nail coatings? She bites her nails so badly that she has to put Band-Aids on them because they hurt so much. What should I do?**

You are correct; her nail biting habit can lead to infections because these damaged areas of the nail can harbor disease causing pathogens. Many studies have confirmed that nurses generally do not wash their hands properly or often enough and this could create an infection risk for patients as well. I mean no offense to nurses, it's a wonderful profession and I admire their work, but studies show they often don't wash their hands as much as they should.

I do understand your desire to help, but applying artificial nail coatings could make matters worse. Nail biters are notorious pickers and often chew on the artificial nail coatings as well. When taken to the extreme you've described, nail biting is a compulsive behavior, so simply applying a nail coating is not likely to address the compulsive behavior. Bacteria can also grow in areas where the nail coating is peeling, cracking or chipping. The key to keeping nail coatings safe is to keep them in good shape and avoiding service breakdown. When this is done, I agree with you, the surface of an artificial nail is much less likely to harbor pathogens than the surface of the natural nail plate.

However, you should be very cautious about applying the nail coatings to any exposed living tissue. If the nail bed is exposed as a result of the client's actions, I don't recommend that you apply these products to either exposed or broken skin. Doing so increases the potential that the client can develop an adverse skin reaction. These types of reactions cause skin damage that can also harbor pathogens, so these types of conditions should also be avoided.

**22:3 What is the reason that UV gel polish shrinks? I see it pull back from the edges when it cures. It seems to be different colors and different customers? Why would that be?**

What you are calling "pull back" may be the effects of shrinkage. All nail coatings shrink when they cure, some more than others. In general, the more thoroughly a nail coating cures, the more it will shrink. Here's why shrinkage is related to curing: the molecules in the coating are linking together and therefore becoming much closer to each other, which leads to shrinkage. That's what happens when millions of molecules that make up a nail coating suddenly come closer together. So a small amount of shrinkage is completely normal and unavoidable. Whenever any type of nail coating shrinks, its edges pull back and will recede toward the center. The more it shrinks, the more it will pull back.

UV gel polish shrinks as it cures, but so can any type of UV cured nail coating. Shrinkage is also determined by "how" these UV coats are cured. Over-curing can cause more shrinkage which may be seen as increased pull back from the edges. As I said, shrinkage of nail coatings always occurs to some degree for all types of nail coatings, that's normal, however excessive shrinkage can cause service breakdown.

Over-curing of UV nail coatings and excessive shrinkage can be caused by using an incorrect nail lamp. Under-curing often leads to much less shrinkage and therefore less pull back. However under-cured nail coatings can pick up stains more easily, are less durable and their filings are more likely to cause adverse skin reactions, under-curing should be avoided. UV gel colors created a special challenge because certain shades or colors can block UV penetration.

To achieve various shades or colors, certain colorants and pigments must be used and these may be prone to absorbing or blocking UV energy. Also, these colorants or pigments may be needed in higher concentrations to ensure full coverage or opacity. The increased concentration of these can affect ease of application, making it more difficult to apply these particular shades or colors. In other words, some shades or colors must be formulated differently from others, in order to account for these effects. Various special additives may then be needed to make application easier. Also, more photoinitiators (PI) may be required to ensure proper cure. Different shades of UV gel polish often have different formulations and this can affect ease of application and may increase "shrinkage".

In general, UV cure nail coating tends to shrink more than any other type nail coating. Cyanoacrylate monomer based coating such as fiberglass wraps, the so-called "no-light" gels or nail tip adhesives tend to shrink the least. Mostly this is because cyanoacrylate monomers do not form "cross-linked" structures when they cure, as do UV systems and the "two-part" systems often referred to as "liquid and powder". Cross-linking improves strength and durability, but excessive cross-linking increases the shrinkage and reduces overall durability. Liquid and powder systems are right in the middle, shrinking less than UV systems, but more than cyanoacrylate based products.

The amount of "pull back" from the edges can be made worse when the nail plate is not properly prepared in order to remove surface oils. Surface oils can block adhesion to the surface of the nail plate and can contribute to pull back as well. If the nail coating doesn't adhere well to the surface of the nail plate, it can pull back more easily when the coating shrinks. The opposite is true, as well. Coatings that adhere very well may not pull back as much, even though they have a considerable amount of shrinkage. Shrinkage happens "during" the curing process, not "before" curing and that's important to understand. Some mistakenly believe the amount of pull back is related to working too quickly or too slowly. Pull back isn't affected by how fast or slow you work, so it doesn't help to "allow time" for shrinkage to occur before you cure. That's not going to help.

The amount of shrinkage is directly related to the type of ingredients in the formula and their concentrations, as well as the wavelength and intensity of UV exposure. It's easier to formulate a UV curing product that shrinks excessively and a whole lot harder to formulate one that doesn't shrink excessively. You can't control how the product is formulated, but you can ensure that you are properly curing and cleaning the nail plate.

**24:1 Doug, if a UV gel "burns like crazy" under the UV lamp, students are told that it is because the gel is "cattivi". Which in Italian means "bad"? In my opinion the problem is more related to the way the gel is being used during application. What do you think?"**

I do agree with this. When UV gels are properly applied and cured, they can become warm, but they are NOT supposed to "burn like crazy". Of course, this assumes the students are using a quality, brand-named UV gel that is well formulated, properly applied and then cured as directed by the manufacturer in the correct lamp. Manufacturers take steps to ensure their UV gel doesn't "burn like crazy". So if anyone is getting this amount of excessive heat, then it would seem they are NOT properly applying and/or curing.

If the UV gel is applied too thickly or cured in an unsuitable nail lamp, then excessive heating may occur. These are the two most common reasons for this to happen. When the "correct" thickness of UV gel is applied, they may become warm, but when applied too thickly more heat is released and the nail can become very warm. When done in combination with a nail lamp that releases too much UV energy for curing the UV gel, then over heating becomes very likely to occur. That's because one symptom of over-curing a UV gel is the release of excessive amounts of heat.

This type of burning can cause the nail plate to separate from the nail bed to create an open space, which is called "onycholysis" (on-EE-ko-LY-sis). Once onycholysis occurs, the nail bed may later become infected and should the condition worsen, this can eventually lead to complete loss of the nail plate unless proper care is taken to reverse the condition. Once onycholysis occurs, the nail plate should be kept short and clients will have to be careful not to injure them until they can grow out again. When the hyponychium seal under the free edge is reestablished, then the nail plate should continue to grow normally. Depending on the severity of the onycholysis, this condition may take one or two months to resolve itself. During that time, clients should be instructed to wear gloves and to keep their nails clean, dry and to do everything they can to prevent catching the nail on objects which could pry the back plate and lead to even more nail bed separation. Keeping the nail plate short will help prevent additional damage.

The other possible reason the UV gel may feel too hot could be because the nail bed has been friction burned by overly-aggressive filing techniques. This is often done when nail technicians use heavy handed filing techniques, in other words, using too much downward force on the nail file. When an electric file is improperly used on the nail plate, the results can be friction burns to the nail bed. Friction burns causes the nail bed to become super-sensitive to even normal and acceptable levels of warming that normally wouldn't be a concern. Client's natural nails should be gently and carefully filed and not treated roughly while being filed. Also, be sure to apply UV gels in thin layers and cure them with the correct UV nail lamp in order to assure a proper cure.

**25:2 I just wanted to have this clear. We get an inhibition layer because 50% of the UV gel is cured and the other 50% is not cured. We remove the 50% top layer that's not cured with alcohol. It doesn't cure because of the oxygen in the air?**

I am concerned if only 50% of your UV gel is curing. This may indicate that something needs to be corrected. You are correct, this sticky surface layer is properly called the "inhibition layer", because of how it is formed. When oxygen is present, it blocks the ends of the growing polymer chains to prevent or "inhibit" these chains from becoming any longer. This is sometimes incorrectly called the "dispersion layer", but that term refers to how oils spreads out over the surface of water or concrete pavement and is not a correct way to describe this sticky layer.

Rather than growing long enough to cause the UV gel to harden, these shortened chains remain in a semi-hardened form that it is easily removed from the surface of the hardened gel layer that is underneath it. This happens because the lack of oxygen at deeper levels allows this lower layer to cure and harden. Faster curing UV gels usually have a thinner inhibition layer, while slower curing UV gels can have a thicker layer. This happens because faster curing UV gel will harden before oxygen has time to block the chains and prevent them from growing.

It is important to understand that if the nail lamp emits too little UV or emits UV of the incorrect wavelength range, curing will be slower and the inhibition layer will become thicker. If the UV bulbs in the nail lamp need to be changed, this will also create a thicker layer as well. An inhibition layer that is 50% of the total applied product seems like an excessive amount to me. Assuming that you are using the nail lamp recommended by the manufacturer of the UV gel, I'd recommend changing your bulbs, especially if they haven't been changed in a few months and the nail lamp is used regularly.

Make sure you're using the correct UV bulbs for your nail lamp. The UV bulbs may look the same, but bulbs from different manufacturers can vary significantly. The range of wavelengths and the intensity of the UV could be much lower than what is needed for proper cure. Low quality UV bulbs breakdown/degrade much more quickly than high quality bulbs and will need to be changed more often It is wise to only use the UV bulbs recommended by the manufacturer of the UV gel in order to help ensure proper cure. Look at the part number printed on the UV bulb to ensure you're re-ordering the proper replacement.

Dirty or gel coated UV bulbs will not properly cure the nail coating so make sure to avoid this by cleaning your bulbs often. Bulbs contaminated with cured gel can be turned over "ONCE". Be sure to warn clients NOT to allow their nails to touch the bulbs or the LED diodes/bulbs in a UV nail lamp, since this can drastically lower their effectiveness. The same is true for the reflective material inside the nail lamp. Make sure it is clean and not coated with cured UV gel. If the reflecting material is dirty or in poor condition, this can also affect curing. Improper placement of the hands in the lamp can also lead to improper cure and may create thicker inhibition layers. This layer will thicken even if repeatedly pulling hands out of the nail lamp, which is not a proper cure. The hands aren't exposed to the correct amount of UV. These are the main factors that can contribute to excessive inhibition layers. If you notice this layer becoming thicker than normal, use the mentioned tips to find out why and correct the situation.

As I said, 50% of the coating seems excessive to me. I would expect the inhibition layer of a properly cured UV gel nail to be 25% or less of the total applied layers. Under-cured UV gels is a leading cause of adverse skin reactions for nail technicians, since they are repeatedly exposed to dusts and filings. So don't ignore the problem when excessively thick inhibition layers begin to form. Find out why and fix the issue. Don't forget to take appropriate care to avoid contact with the inhibition layer; prolonged or repeated contact with this layer can also lead to adverse skin reactions.

### 27:3 I was using an anti-fungal UV gel and my client got an infection. Why didn't it work?

In my view, there is no such thing as an anti-fungal UV gel and no cosmetic company should be making such claims. Cosmetics are for beautification of the body or improving physical appearance. No cosmetic product can claim to prevent infections. That is NOT an allowed cosmetic claim and this is true for most, if not all countries. This is certainly true in the US, the European Union, Canada and Australia, to name a few. Products designed to prevent infections are medical drugs or medication and NOT cosmetics. This is true for lotions, creams, sprays, gels whatever form they come in.

When a cosmetic product claims that it treats, cures, controls or prevents any type of infection, it ceases to be a cosmetic and is now a medical drug or medicine, it can NO longer be sold as a cosmetic product. It is not likely that any cosmetic nail coating, including UV gel can prevent any type of nail infection. Some may contain anti-fungal or anti-bacterial ingredients, but that only prevents the growth of these types of microorganisms inside the product container. In other words, they are preservatives and are incapable of preventing nail infections.

If you want to prevent nail infections in the salon, here's the best way: Make sure your client's hands and fingernails are clean. It is important to clean and disinfect everything that comes in contact with a client's skin. Finally, never perform services on clients with active infections of the skin or nails. Only a medical professional can properly determine if a visible infection is active or not. If clients show symptoms of having a visible infection, it is best to refuse services until the symptoms disappear or a medical professional determines their condition is not contagious.

## 28:1 How about products that say they can repair the nail and yet are placed under UV? For example, base coat repair systems or those that claim to seal together the layers of the nail plate?

There is a lot of confusion about these types of products. Not surprisingly, several products exist which can indeed repair "physical" damage to the nail plate. Cosmetics can appropriately claim to repair physical damage or to improve the physical condition or appearance of the nail. Cosmetic products, including nail enhancements and coating can stop cracks, fill in grooves or pits and repair peeling nails, as well as to prevent these from occurring and to protect the nail plate from damage. These are all proper cosmetic product functions. However, they can NOT claim to treat, reverse or prevent any medical conditions.

Only medical drugs or medicines can perform these functions.

There is a big difference between the "physical" condition and the "medical" condition. Be careful not to confuse these. Cosmetics are NOT medical drugs or medication and can't claim to be. Medicines prevent infections, cosmetics do not.

### 37:3 I'm confused about doing a UV gel manicure with water or without water? What is the proper procedure? I have been told both.

There is no shortage of opinions about this topic, but there is a shortage of the facts and proper understanding. I believe that clients should wash their hands before every service. This exposes the nails to water for about 20 seconds, if they properly wash. Twenty seconds is not a problem and will not affect adhesion. However, this will significantly lower the risks of nail infections in the salon. In my view, not asking clients to wash their hands is risky and increases the potential for nail infections in the salon, so the hands should always be washed before every service.

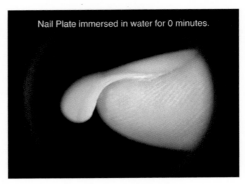

Nail Plate immersed in water for 0 minutes.

What is the effect of soaking the nail plate in water? That really depends on the nail plates. Thick healthy nail plates with normally good adhesion to nail coating products will be largely unaffected when soaked in water or when a water manicure is performed. However, clients with thin, weak or highly flexible nail plates would probably do better without a water manicure. Normally, it will take about 60 seconds for a nail plate to absorb any substantial amount of water. The longer the nail plate is soaked, the more water will be absorbed. All of this absorbed water can cause the nail plate to swell and change shape. Why? As the water molecules crowd in between the layers of the nail plate, this lubricates the layers and allows them to slide past each other while at the same time forcing the layers apart.

Nail Plate immersed in water for 3 minutes.

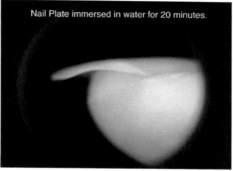

Nail Plate immersed in water for 20 minutes.

Nail Plate immersed in water for 10 minutes.

This results in making the nail plate more flexible and more likely to swell and change shape. The plate could curl up, flatten out or even twist... depending on its original shape. This happens because the water content of the nail can double becoming 25-

30%. Then when the nail plate returns to its normal moisture content of about 15-18%, the nail plate will then revert back to its normal shape. Nail coatings applied to a swollen nail plate can't be expected to adhere well to a moving surface that's changing shape. As the plates dries, the nail coating will be stretched as the nail plate goes through its shape shifting. When the plate reverts back to its normal shape, this can put stress on the nail coating and cause it to lose adhesion to the natural nail and may result in chipping, peeling or cracking.

There is no black and white answer, since much of this depends on the client's nails. Thinner or more flexible nail plates will be much more affected than thicker nail plates which aren't as flexible. This is always why it is so important for nail professionals to understand this type of information. Otherwise, they become a victim of "she said/he said". This is often just a war of uninformed opinions. It's better to make decisions based on the facts.

# UV Nail Lamps

## Section 3

### 1: Special Topic Are UV Nail Lamps Safe?

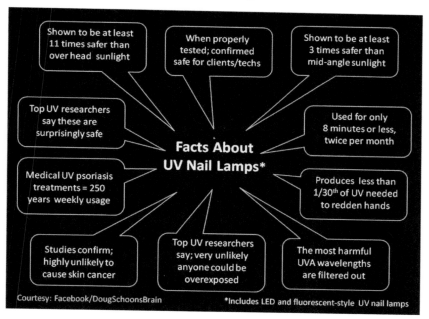

Shown to be at least 11 times safer than over head sunlight

When properly tested; confirmed safe for clients/techs

Shown to be at least 3 times safer than mid-angle sunlight

Top UV researchers say these are surprisingly safe

**Facts About UV Nail Lamps***

Used for only 8 minutes or less, twice per month

Medical UV psoriasis treatments = 250 years weekly usage

Produces less than 1/30th of UV needed to redden hands

Studies confirm; highly unlikely to cause skin cancer

Top UV researchers say; very unlikely anyone could be overexposed

The most harmful UVA wavelengths are filtered out

Courtesy: Facebook/DougSchoonsBrain          *Includes LED and fluorescent-style UV nail lamps

Yes, they absolutely are safe! Several high-quality scientific studies performed by world-leading experts have demonstrated that UV nail lamps are safe, but some haven't gotten the word. Unfortunately, most of the information that has been released by the media is misleading and/or deceptive. To confuse matters more, several poorly performed scientific studies by amateurs using improper test equipment have created confusion. However, the studies performed by the top UV experts have provided great clarity. There studies show that both LED-style and Fluorescent-style UV nail lamps are safe as used in nail salons. Now, when I refer to "UV nail lamps", I'm collectively referring to both LED and Fluorescent-style UV nail lamps. Both emit UV and both have been found to be safe for use in nail salons.

These scientific studies confirmed that when UV nail lamps are properly measured, they are at least three times safer than sunlight that is directly overhead and at least eleven times safer than mid-angle sunlight. Mid-angle sunlight occurs around 3 PM, depending on your location in the world. This is when the sun is halfway between being directly overhead and setting on the horizon. For many years, dermatologists have told us that mid-angle sunlight is unlikely to cause sunburn and is considered safe, even without sunscreen. Yes, UV nail lamps are at least three times safer!

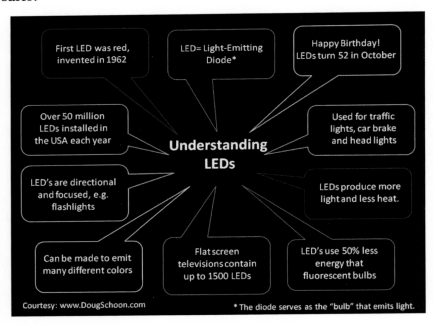

Courtesy: www.DougSchoon.com          * The diode serves as the "bulb" that emits light.

These nail lamps aren't accidentally safe; they are designed to be safe. For example, they only emit UV-A which is the safest part of the UV spectrum and more than 40% of the UV-A range is eliminated completely; no UV-B or UV-C is used to cure nail coatings. These nail lamps are filtered to allow only the safest UV-

A wavelengths to pass; filtering out all of the UV-A wavelengths that cause the most concern. The low intensity of UV emitted in combination with filtering out these wavelengths of concern is the primary reason these nail lamps are considered to be safer than natural sunlight. A client's hands would have to be placed under the most powerful UV nail lamps for two hours to even redden the skin.

Interestingly, doctors have been providing medical treatments for psoriasis using UV for many years and consider these treatments to be very safe. When scientific researchers compared UV nail services to the skin exposure from medical UV psoriasis treatments, it was determined that a nail client would have to receive 250 years of weekly UV manicures to equal the risks associated with just one course of these safe medical psoriasis treatments. This is why one of the world-leading experts in UV effects on skin, Dr. Robert Sayre says of doctors who suggest these nail lamps may not be safe, *"Doctors are grossly over exaggerating exposures"*. Dr. Sayre tested a wide range of UV nail lamps using internationally accepted standards and measurement equipment to make this safe use determination.

UV nail lamps are used for eight minutes or less, twice per month, so your clients have a much greater risk of UV exposure from the sun while driving their car to the salon and back. As long as nail professionals follow instructions and heed all warnings, it is highly unlikely they will be overexposed to unsafe levels of UV.

Low levels of UV exposure are considered both safe and necessary to health. It is a common myth that sunlight contains vitamin D, when it does not. When our skin is exposed to UV, the skin begins to manufacture vitamin D, which is essential to healthy living. Without low levels of UV exposure, people often develop vitamin D deficiencies which can create a wide range of serious adverse health effects. So clearly, there are safe levels of UV skin exposure that are essential for healthy living. In short, UV nail lamps DO NOT exceed a safe level, which is why Dr. Sayre says this about UV nail lamps in general, "this UV source properly belongs in the least risky of all categories" and "UV nail lamps are safer than natural sunlight or sunlamps." Don't be fooled by misinformation.

## 6:1 I've read your reports and understand that UV nail lamps are safe for my clients. But, what should I tell someone with a history of skin cancer?

This is a great question. I talked in detail about the safety of all nail lamps in another question. Scientific evidence shows these lamps are safe as used. Some clients are likely to remain skeptical and may wish to cover the back of their hands with an opaque cloth or other material. That's OK! There are a variety of solutions, I've seen special UV blocking disposable gloves which are now sold to salons that are extraordinarily effective at completely blocking UV and of course, a 15+ SPF broad spectrum sunscreen will also virtually eliminate UV exposure. In the case of a client with previous history of skin cancer, I'd recommend any of the solutions above which will block UV exposure and should give this person peace of mind. Since this is likely an on-going medical issue, they should seek the advice of their physician before considering an activity, indoor or outdoor, that involves UV exposure, including UV nail services.

## 6: Myth: Calcium is good for your nails.

I don't know of any evidence to demonstrate that oral ingestion of calcium does anything positive for nails, at all! Nail plates do contain a very small amount of calcium, but that likely comes from the water we wash our hands with. Calcium is found only on surface of the nail plate, and not in deeper layers, which further supports that the calcium comes from hand washing. To my knowledge, the nail plate doesn't need calcium and doesn't benefit from it at all. Of course, should any convincing evidence become available to support this seemingly silly notion, I'm happy to review and consider that info, until then I would not recommend calcium supplements since they don't appear to benefit the nail. The same is true for topical application of calcium; this can't help the nail plate either.

## 26:2 Most manufacturers say their LED bulbs are good for 30,000 hours. Can you help break this down for us?

If true, a nail lamp that was on constantly for 40 hours a week would last 14 years. This is NOT a realistic claim considering how these are used. It is a major advantage of UV LED's that they degrade more slowly when compared to fluorescent-type UV bulbs. Fluorescent bulbs begin to degrade after 1-3 months, depending upon usage. Some low quality bulbs lose most of their UV output after a single month of continued use. This is one reason why you should never buy inexpensive generic UV bulbs from the Internet. Only use replacements bulbs that are specifically recommended by the UV gel manufacturer. I've talked to several experts in the field who assured me that the UV LED's will likely emit a consistent amount of UV for at least 3 years, which is pretty good. That's about 12 times longer than what could be expected from even a high quality fluorescent-style bulbs under constant use.

Even so, considering the real-world use of nail lamp you'll likely have to replace your LED-style UV nail lamp every three years anyway. Some nail lamps will last longer and some will need replacing more often depending on A). usage time, B). the quality of the nail lamp, and C). how the nail lamp is treated in the salon. It is misguided to give the lifetime of the UV diodes (bulbs) inside LED-style UV nail lamps. Manufacturers should be taking about the lifetime of the "nail lamp" as a whole, since the diodes can't be replaced. Even so, that's not what will determine how often you'll need to replace the nail lamp.

"Diodes" are the UV emitting bulbs in LED nail lamps. These may become contaminated with UV gel if a client touches them with their uncured nails. Once this occurs, the diode will not emit nearly as much UV. This happens with fluorescentbulbs as well, but they can be turned over and the other side of the bulb used or they are easily replaced. Also, the lamp cord will likely wear out long before 14 years. These lamps aren't like a toasters or microwaves. Toasters don't get put away in a drawer after use or have their cords wrapped around them every day, as nail professionals do- especially those with small nail tables. Mobile nail techs do this even more often.

The cord isn't what often breaks. Breaks usually occur at the connector where the cord goes into the lamp unit. In fact, my experience tells me that the electrical cords are good, on average for three to four years. By then, the outer housing of the lamp will begin to look pretty shabby or possibly become cracked. The electrical components inside that drive the LED's can stop delivering enough power or stop working altogether. When this occurs, the nail lamp won't properly cure the UV gel. The electronic part of the lamp is built to last a long time, but cycling on/off for many years without failure is not very likely for most nail lamps. To my way of thinking, the industry marketers are better off under-promising and over-delivering, not the other way around.

When I was in Europe last month, many nail professionals told me they've heavily used their UV nail lamps for two years and have already needed to replace them. I really doubt the average user will need to replace their lamps every two years, but I don't think you can expect your lamp to last more than five years either, unless it sits on the shelf much of the time. Even so, even if you replace the nail lamp every three years, LEDs are still less expensive than fluorescent-style UV nail lamps. Those who use fluorescent style nail lamps usually need to replace their bulbs about three times a year. Nail lamps generally contain four bulbs, which ends up being twelve bulbs per year or thirty-six bulbs in three years. At $14/bulb that would be $500 just in bulbs. LED bulbs do provide a steadier output of UV than fluorescent bulbs and will do this for a much longer period. Even if you have to replace the LED nail lamp every three years, you're still saving money. Please, do not take my estimates wrong. I am not telling you to start using LED-style UV nail lamps because they are superior; they are only superior when used with a UV gel specifically designed for use with LED-style UV nail lamps. They should NOT be used with UV gels designed for use only with fluorescent-style UV nail lamps. Use only the nail lamp specified by the manufacturers of the UV gel. Never use an LED nail lamp unless the UV gel manufacturer directs you to do so.

**39:1 I've heard what you said about UV exposure, but a few customers are still concerned even after I give them all of your information. Now what? I know you said wearing SPF 15 sunscreen works, but I don't want sunscreen being applied in my salon. Its messy and can cause lifting. So what else can I do?**

That's a good point. As I've replied in other questions, there is no need to be concerned about exposure to UV nail lamps. Not only did two of the world leading scientists in the field of UV and skin exposure perform extensive testing on a wide range of nail lamps and declare them to be "surprisingly safe"; a major university in the USA says UV nail lamps are much safer than treatments dermatologists provide to patents with psoriasis. The medical community says UV psoriasis treatments are a very safe procedure. This research study shows that clients would have to receive 250 years of weekly UV nail services to equal a single course of psoriasis treatment that doctors have been providing their clients for decades. I certainly understand that some clients are highly fearful and even scientific or medical facts will not sway them. When a client is completely closed-minded or unreasonable and won't listen at all, what then? They could benefit from these services, but not if they can't get past their fears. This is becoming more prevalent, because people are exposed to piles of misinformation, mostly on TV or the Internet, and many don't know what to believe so they distrust just about everything.

I still think it is very important to provide clients with the facts, but when they aren't convinced, I get it, and you need other options. I also understand your concerns about sunscreens. They can be messy and what's more, they can cause a loss of adhesion that can lead to lifting if the sunscreen product is not completely removed from the nail plate. When sprayed near the table, sunscreen products can also contaminate tools, implements or even get into nail tip trays or inside product containers. So it is never a good idea to spray sunscreen products near the nail table.

There is another alternative, you can cover the back of the hand. Pretty simple isn't it? In fact, it's such a simple solution it makes me wonder why this controversy ever started. Covering the back of the hand with an opaque material of any color will block the UV and reduce the client's exposure to near zero. If you want to give these clients maximum piece-of-mind, then you can purchase disposable plastic shields that are specially designed to serve as a complete UV protection for the hands, while still allowing UV exposure on the nail coatings, so they can properly cure. These plastic glove UV shields can be found on the internet and shipped directly to your salon, or you can get a pair of cotton gloves and cut out the fingers. The UV shielding plastic sheets have the advantage of being low cost and disposable after a single use, which is a big advantage. Cloth gloves will have to be machine washed with bleach between each client, since anything that comes in contact with the client's skin must be properly cleaned and disinfected before they can be reused or the item must be disposed of into the trash.

# Polish, Other Coatings and Adhesives

## Section 4

### 2: Special Topic- The Toxic Trio Myth"

We've all heard the misleading claims that nail polish is harmful, unless it's "3-Free". The facts are, this was deception from the very beginning. All nail polish can be used safely and that's been true for more than eighty years. Nail polish formulas haven't changed much since the 1930's. How did they so suddenly become dangerous? I don't know anyone who has been harmed by using nail polish, other than it catching fire. Fresh nail polish is flammable- so don't do as my friend did and light up a cigarette immediately after polishing your nails. All nail polishes are safe. Those that market their polish as "safer" are splitting hairs. It's like saying that using an SPF 70 lotion isn't as safe as SPF 80. The fact is both are safe. Don't be concerned about nail polish causing any harm to your health, when used as directed.

How did all of this misinformation about nail polish get started? It started as a clever and highly deceptive marketing campaign by a fear-based activist group. This group created a false safety concern and then cashed in on the donations, claiming they were saving the world from dangerous nail polish! They made exaggerated claims about the ingredients to needlessly frighten the public. For example, they claimed that toluene is dangerous in nail polishes, but that information is contrary to the facts. Toluene was reviewed by the prestigious Cosmetic Review Expert Panel (CIR) and after fairly reviewing all of the scientific information, this panel of world class doctors and scientists determined that toluene is considered safe up to 50% in nail polishes. The European Union did the same testing and concluded that toluene is safe in nail polish up to 25%, which is the concentrations that are typically used. Therefore, independent scientific experts in both the US and EU say that toluene is safe for use in nail polishes.

Then why is toluene no longer in use for this purpose? Manufacturers voluntarily eliminated toluene because it is a volatile organic compound (VOC) and it was found to contribute slightly to ozone depletion. Nail manufacturers wanting to do their part for the environment agreed to replace toluene with other solvents. Even so, these fear-based advocacy groups again deceived the public and pretended that manufacturers change because of toluene's toxicity, which is an outright lie. These same activist groups lie to the news media as well and tell them that even nail polish formulas with <0.1% toluene are still toxic- even though this is contrary to all of the scientific facts. These groups pretend there is no safe amount of anything they say is dangerous. This just shows they don't understand the science or the facts and instead, want the world to be black and white, when this clearly isn't so.

Dibutyl phthalate (DBP) is another example. This ingredient hasn't been used very much at all in nail polish formulas for at least ten years, but that didn't stop these groups from stretching the truth. It is no longer used, even though it has been found to be safe for nail polish applications. Better replacements are now used to increase the wearability of nail polish, which was how DBP functioned in polish. There has NEVER been any credible evidence to show that DPB was harmful in nail polishes. Other phthalates with similar sounding names were determined to be unsuitable for cosmetics, but these were never used in nail polish. The fear mongering activists paint everything with a broad brush, so without evidence they assumed that DBP must also be dangerous. In other words, rather than explain that some phthalates are safe, they decided to scare consumers by telling them that all phthalates are dangerous, again, because they don't understand the facts. They hide their lack of knowledge and reduce everything to black and white. They don't like the scientific facts; they'd rather base their unfair attacks on pure speculation.

Formaldehyde is a gas and can't be added to cosmetics and has never been used in any nail polish as an ingredient. Formaldehyde only exists in tiny traces in a few thousandths of a percent, since that is all that will dissolve into the products. At these levels formaldehyde is safe. These concentrations are close to the amounts that are found naturally in our bodies and our breath. These groups never mention that formaldehyde is natural and organic. Everyday our bodies create formaldehyde and use it to make natural substances and proteins needed for life. The myth that harmful levels are found in nail polish got its start when these foolish activists were confused by the ingredient listing on nail polish bottles. Years ago nail polish manufacturers were required to call the best polymer resin by a name that included the word formaldehyde. The resin was called toluene sulfonamide formaldehyde resin (TSFR). This isn't toluene or formaldehyde. These substances were used to make a completely different ingredient and because they were made using these ingredients, it was assumed that they were in the polish. However, when this resin is used, the nail polish might contain 0.0005%, so you can't say technically say they are "formaldehyde-free", but for all practical purposes, they are indeed free of formaldehyde. Because of the misinformation spread by these fear-mongers, nail manufacturers worked behind the scene to have this misleading name corrected. Some may still use the old name for this ingredient, but this is slowly changing as manufacturers update their labels.

You can find more fact-based information about nail polish by visiting the Nail Manufacturers Council on Safety's website at http://www.probeauty.org/nmc/. You will learn that all nail polish is safe and always has been. Don't be fooled by fear-based marketers selling 3-free, 4-free, 5-free or 6-free nail polishes. These nail polishes are not safer than any other nail polish. To ensure the safe use of nail polish, follow directions and heed all warnings. For instance, keep nail polish and remover solvents out of the reach of children and away from sources of heat or flames.

## 10:3 If I polish the nails of children, should I use water based polish instead? What are your thoughts on those types of products?

First, nail polish doesn't absorb through the nail plate and won't get into your blood stream, those are just "Myths turned into Tricks", as I'll explain below. Secondly, water-based nail polish is not safer than other types of nail polishes. All nail polishes can be used safely. The solvent "water" is used to replace other solvents. Also, the thickeners and other ingredients must be water soluble, but water-based nail polishes can only claim to be "water-based", if at least 51% of the solvents used is water. Nothing is wrong with this, unless in the marketing of these products it is wrongfully claimed that other nail polish solvents are "harmful" to consumers.

There is little reason to believe that any nail polish solvents are harmful, especially given these nail polish formulas have been in use for about 80 years. If you look at records, nail polish has a very long history of safe use. Anything can be made to sound scary and any trickster can come up with clever ways to manipulate truth. I'll give you an example. If I wanted to scare you away from water-based nail polishes, I could have answered by stating emphatically, "What? Don't you know that water has killed millions of people, more than all the other solvents in nail polish combined?" Or, "Are you crazy, didn't you know that water is a powerful chemical solvent that's been linked to many deaths and unimaginable levels of human suffering?" or, "Don't you know that water based nail polishes must contain preservatives?"

Each of these examples are true statements, so what? This doesn't mean water isn't safe when used in nail polish. Of course water is a powerful solvent; it's not called the Universal Solvent for nothing. It dissolves more things than any other solvent. Unless specially packaged and sealed in air tight containers, any water based cosmetics need some sort of preservative to prevent the growth of bacteria and fungi. Preservatives help ensure that such products are safe for use. So, it's not a negative at all that water-based polishes must contain a preservative, but non-water based nail polishes are self-disinfecting which is an advantage.

I could say, "Do you want a nail polish that can grow bacteria?" Or "Do you want one that doesn't contain that potentially deadly chemical water AND it contains no preservatives, unlike those water-based nail polishes?" See how easily the truth can be manipulated? Watch for this clever marketing trick from the dark-side and don't be fooled. All nail polish is safe if used properly, according to manufacturer's directions and all warnings are heeded. I hope you have many days of happy polishing!

### 10:5 Aren't vegan claims for foods and not for cosmetics? What about vegan nail polish?

Many agree with you, but there are several sides to this issue to consider. I've talked to vegans about this and they make a good point. They feel that if a product contains animal by-products, even though it's not a food, they don't want to use them. So some dietary vegans also look for so-called vegan cosmetics. To my way of thinking, that makes this a valid claim. Even so, very few nail polishes use any animal by-products. So most nail polishes could claim to be vegan, but don't because they don't consider it a meaningful claim. I'm using the term nail polish properly; to mean varnish, lacquer or enamel.

Many years ago, some nail polishes used to contain fish scales, which created sparkle effects, but that's not been done in years. Superior synthetic sparkle effects are now used instead. There are only two other possible sources of animal by-products that I'm aware of:

1.  A few red shades of nail polishes still use "carmine" as a pigment, which is extracted from insects. That bothers some vegans who consider even insects as animals. This colorant can cause moderate to serious adverse skin reaction in sensitive individuals, so in the US, any cosmetic using carmine and designed for skin contact must carry a warning. Nail polishes aren't

applied to the skin, so this isn't a likely problem for this application, whereas skin creams for sensitive skin should probably avoid this ingredient.

2. Some naturally occurring clays used to control the thickness of nail polish, are modified with a small amount of tallow (from cows) to increase effectiveness. However, manufacturers tell me that very few brands of nail polishes continue to use these types of thickeners, since most have changed to plant modified clays. So the only real difference between vegan and all other nail polishes is that they don't use carmine as a colorant and they avoid the clay that's treated with small amounts of animal tallow and of course I have an open mind about this issue and respect vegans who look for vegan cosmetics, but I will say this, being a "vegan nail polish" does NOT make these nail polish any safer than other nail polishes. This is a personal lifestyle preference and not related in any way to safety, but I don't think many understand this. That's because the public has been tricked into thinking some types of nail polish are not safe, when in fact ALL nail polish can be used safely, I don't know of any exceptions.

## 11:6 Why do nail polish top coats get stringy when applied?

It's all about the solvent, in the top coat. Top coats are blends of several solvents, not just one type and often are 20-30% or more of the formula. Some solvents evaporate quickly and can escape from open top coat containers, leaving the slower evaporating solvents behind. This causes a slow shift in the ratio of these solvents, which alters the top coat away from its original composition. Not only that, the total concentration of solvents is slowly getting lower, which means that all other ingredients become more concentrated. That leads to even further changes the composition. The polymers used in the top coats are chosen because they can harden into smooth films within a relatively short time. Before the film hardens, it goes through a stage where it isn't a flowing liquid, but it isn't yet a hard solid. This "in-between stringy phase" is what you get just before the film hardens. If this is happening in the bottle, it's likely because excessive amounts of solvents have escaped from the container, and the top coat is beginning to slowly harden in the container. Keep the caps tightly sealed and containers tightly closed with the necks clean to prevent premature evaporation of solvents.

**12:1 I was always led to believe that a nail resin and glue are different. If this is correct, what are the differences and how do I know which to use?**

This question illustrates a big problem in the beauty industry in general and demonstrates how confusing nail industry terminology can be. Why does this continue to happen? Largely because nail product marketers too often use the incorrect terms to describe their products or services, which further reinforces the use of these terms. The trade magazines sometimes do this as well. Don't get me wrong, I'm not blaming nail marketers and the magazines, they are just responding to the words nail professionals use every day. That's their job!

It seems to me that much of the incorrect terminology comes from nail schools, educators and veteran nail technicians who don't keep up with the latest educational information. That's why I focus on providing this type of information to educators. They are our best hope for improving this situation and the industry. In practical terms, resin and glue are the same and it is a misunderstanding to think they are different.

How did this misunderstanding occur? To understand, we have to travel back to ancient times. The word glue actually refers to animal-based adhesives. Glue's were originally made from proteins extracted from animal hides, horns and hooves. In the 30's that new-fangled Elmer's Glue was developed. It was a breakthrough. This adhesive used a protein found in milk called casein. Protein-based glues have been used since ancient times to adhere things together and for thousands of years, all was well. Confusion began in the late 40's when Elmer glue changed formulas from milk protein to a synthetic polymer called polyvinyl acetate or PVA.

This polymer belongs to a unique class of polymers that are called "resins". Originally the term "resin" was used to describe the thick, sticky sap that oozes from certain trees, bushes and plants. The natural resins were also used by the ancients as both as glues and as protective, water-proof coatings for wood, leather and cloth. They were even used by early artists to adhere pigments to walls to make cave paintings. Interestingly, when Elmer's changed their formula the term "resin" came to be used to describe synthetic substances that could mimic the thick and sticky properties of natural resins.

How does this apply to nails? Nail adhesives, wraps, resins and no-light gels are all based on a synthetic monomer called cyanoacrylate which is not very thick or sticky. Since this monomer will eventually harden to form a sticky polymer, they are called resins; even though this is not technically correct, since they aren't resins, they are monomers. What's the bottom line? These products are no more glues than they are resins. I'm alright with either term because they are not "wrong". Even so, rather than use inaccurate and incorrect definitions that confuse, why not use a more professional term such as, "adhesives" when you are referring to "adhering things together" and the term "cyanoacrylate monomer" when these are used as a nail coating, rather than "resin". Consider this as well, which of these would clients have a greater respect for or be more impressed by? I think the answer is obvious.

The main value of using professional terminology is that it would end a lot of confusion and elevate the nail salon industry in the public's eye. Getting the industry on this course has to start with nail educators. They must learn and then teach the correct terminology, as well as, the importance of using the correct terms. Until this is done, this situation isn't going to change any time soon. If you're a nail educator, please do your part to ensure that correct terminology is taught and used. Explain the benefits of this to your students and demonstrate a high standard. That's what it will take to unify this industry under a common and agreed upon set of terms.

## 11:10 How do nail polish drying drops and sprays work?

To understand why they work, you must understand why nail polish dries. First, you need to know something. Molecules are really small. Many millions of molecules can fit on the head of a pin. Even the most advanced microscopes could never directly see them or watch them move. Only special highly advanced devices can come anywhere close to doing this. So, we'll just pretend to have microscopic vision and can see molecules. If you use this microscope vision, you could look down into the freshly applied nail polish layer and see that there were millions of molecules shaped much like playing cards used in games. These cards would be mostly standing on their edges and piled on top of each other to form many layers. These molecules would not be found just floating free in solvent, instead they would be randomly stacked to form a crazy looking "house of cards." This house of cards would be only semi-stable and would slowly fall apart as the solvents evaporate. As the polish dried, this house of cards would begin to fall down in slow motion until all the cards are lying flat on their sides. In other words, as the nail polish dries and solvents evaporate away these tiny "playing-card-shaped" thickener molecules settle onto the nail plate, on their sides, lying flat as possible. This is one reason why dry nail polish forms a thinner layer than when wet. Some of this loss of thickness is due to the solvents evaporating away. Most is due to thickener molecules settling into new positions and flattening against the nail plate in piles.

How do nail dryer drops and sprays work? They contain ingredients that target the thickener molecules to cause their "house of cards" to fall very, very rapidly, instead of in slow motion. As the thickener molecules pile up on the nail plate, this pushes the solvents to the surface. The solvents then blend with ingredients in the drops or spray and evaporate away. Now you can see why I first explained how traditional solvent based nail polishes dry. All that a nail polish dryer does is to slightly speed up the process. These dryers do not completely remove the nail polish solvents, so the layer of nail polish will still take a while before it is fully hardened. Even so, polish dryers will knock a good ten to fifteen minutes from the initial drying process.

### 26:4 Some nail polish colors stain my client's nails, why does this happen and what can I do to prevent this?

Wearing a basecoat underneath nail polish does more than improve adhesion and wearability. They can also protect the nail plate from staining, especially on nails with cracks, pits or other types of surface damage. Any type of damaged area on the surface of the nail is more likely to allow certain colorants in nail polish to absorb into the upper layers. When this occurs, the colorants can become trapped and will concentrate to create a visible stain. Of course nail polish colorants are safe to wear, but some may be more likely to stain than others.

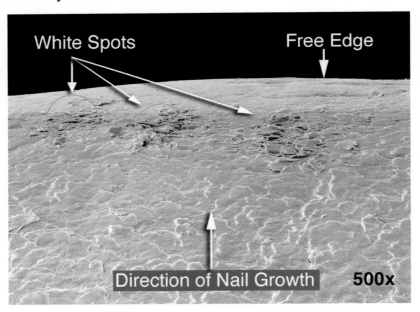

There are three different reds and one yellow colorant that have been reported as the most likely to stain the nail plate. The reds colorants are listed on product ingredient label as Red no. 6, 7, or 34. In the European Union, all three of these red colorants would be sold under their "colour index" or CI number, which is 15850. Usually, "CI" is not listed before the number and only the colour index number appears on the label. The yellow that is reported to cause a lot of staining is Yellow #5 Lake, which is listed on European ingredient labels as CI 19140.

These may appear in your client's favourite shade. If they do, what should you do to avoid staining? The best ways to prevent stains are to always wear basecoats under the nail polish and to keep the surface of the nail plate healthy and damage-free. A good way to keep the nail plate damage-free is to avoid over filing the nail plate and remember "Less is More" when it comes to filing. Never force or scrape tightly bonded residual pieces of nail coatings from the surface. Doing so can cause small pits or microscopic cracks that increase the chance of staining. (Image shows damaged nail cells where color might deposit)

## 27:2 I was wondering if you could shed any light on the system my brother has applied to his nails. It looks like a gel is applied and then dipped into acrylic powder?

I get a lot of questions about products that look like a "gel" when applied, but are then dipped into a powder. These are called "powder gels", however this same name is used to describe two different types of nail coatings. In other words, there are two different nail services that are both considered to be "powder gels". One example is when the surface of a UV gel coating is sprinkled with acrylic powder before UV curing. Why is this done? This isn't likely to enhance any of the properties of a UV gel coating, or make it any more durable. Some claim this makes the nail coating more susceptible to solvents and therefore easier to remove. Using UV gel in this way is an improvement over original "dip powder" systems that were first popular in New York City salons during the early 1990's. Versions of this original dip systems are still in use today. Originally salons began applying cyanoacrylate adhesives (glue) to the nail plate, after which the entire finger was dipped into their acrylic powder used for liquid and powder enhancements.

These are non-UV curing systems and were called "dip powder" systems. They are based mostly on cyanoacrylate monomers, which are members of the acrylic chemical family. Cyanoacrylate nail coatings lack strength/durability and they breakdown quickly. Cyanoacrylate monomers link together to form hard polymers; so why do they breakdown so readily? Cyanoacrylate based polymers are highly sensitive to water/moisture and don't last long when repeatedly or excessively exposed to it in any fashion. That is why the newer powder systems rely instead on UV gels, rather than cyanoacrylate monomers. UV gels are mostly based on urethane acrylate resins, which are also members of the acrylic chemical family. Both urethane acrylate and urethane methacrylate resins form hard polymer nail coatings that are much more water-resistant and durable than cyanoacrylate-based nail coatings.

Despite some limitations, cyanoacrylate monomers (aka resin) are great for many purposes in nail salons, e.g. "wrap" nail coatings with embedded fiberglass or silk. Modified cyanoacrylates are used as "glue" to adhere artificial nail tips or decorative objects to the natural nail. What makes cyanoacrylates extra sensitive to moisture and solvents? They don't form cross-linked polymer structures upon cure! Examples of cross-linked nail coatings are two-part monomer liquid/polymer powder and UV cured nail coatings. Cross-links between the polymer chains make nail coatings highly resistant to attack by water or other solvents. Exposures to warm water, e.g. Jacuzzis or hot baths, will accelerate the breakdown of cyanoacrylate nail coatings and adhesives. Fiberglass or silk material is embedded into the cyanoacrylates monomer to increase the strength and durability of the nail coating. In contrast, dip powder systems replace fiberglass/silk material with acrylic powder to provide some additional strength. Without using fiberglass, silk or acrylic powder, cyanoacrylate nail coatings are not nearly as durable and would make poor nail coatings.

In my opinion, it is a big negative for dip powder systems to require clients to dip their finger into a powder. This is viewed by many, including some government regulators and clients, to be unsanitary. Salons that dip multiple clients' fingers into the same powder have an increased risk of transmitting an infectious microorganism that can lead to an infection. If your region has regulations against "double dipping" into cosmetics to perform client services, then a powder dip system may be in violation of those regulations. Some of the newer systems very wisely recommend that the acrylic powder be sprinkled over the top of the nail, rather than dipping. I don't recommend dipping multiple clients nails into the same powder, especially given that many salons don't require clients to wash their hands or nails before receiving a service.

Finally, it is a myth that some cyanoacrylates release formaldehyde when they undergo service breakdown. This is false and extremely unlikely to occur in the salon setting. Cyanoacrylates in general are considered safe for salon use. I do believe any of these types of nail services are generally safe when properly used, but I also believe that nail professionals should always perform their nail services in a sanitary fashion and this responsibility should be their first priority.

## 28:5 Can you please tell me if I can thin out my UV gel polishes, base and top coat?

You can, but I don't recommend it. You'll never restore these products back to their original condition. The added solvents will most likely affect how the product cures and could lower long term durability of the coating. That's why I never developed a product thinner during all my years in product development. It is far better to prevent evaporation from occurring in the first place, rather than to fix the product. How? Tightly replace the cap on the product container when you're done using it. If the cap isn't tight, solvents can slowly escape which allows the product to slowly thicken in the container.

Don't let polish dry or accumulate in the threads around the neck of the bottle or inside the cap. If product hardens in the treads, this prevents a tight seal which can allow solvents to slowly escape. If the manufacturer of the UV gel product directs you to use a thinner, use only the thinner they recommend and no other.

Remember, when it comes to the use of thinners. Less is more! Avoid using any more thinner than is absolutely needed. Finally, I don't think a brand of thinners should be sold for use with any product. In my opinion, manufacturers can't really know how the thinner will affect other manufacturer's UV gels and likely they don't really care. They just want you to buy their thinner. Buyer Beware!

# Contamination Control

## Section 5

### 1:1 In nail technician's terms, what is the difference between sanitation, disinfection and sterilization.

Sanitation is another word for "cleaning". Removing visible contamination and debris and dramatically lowering the number of "germs" on the surface. Hand-washing, brushing teeth and washing any object with soap and water are examples. Cleaning is the first and most important step for controlling pathogens.

Disinfectants are deactivated by soap films, dirt, grease or oil, which is why it's critical that implements be completely clean before they are disinfected. Disinfection is the destruction of viruses, bacteria and fungi on surfaces that have come in contact with a client's skin. Salon disinfectants are generally 99.99% effective. It is false and misleading to claim that disinfectants don't work. When they are properly used, they are extremely effective. Disinfection is only for non-living surfaces since disinfectants are damaging to living skin and may lead to irritation or allergic reactions.

Sterilization is the complete destruction of all microscopic life on a surface.

Hospitals use sterilization on surgical tools, but not everything can be sterilized. Surfaces such as table tops and foot spas can't fit into an autoclave and must be disinfected, so even if you use an autoclave, you will still need to also use disinfectants in the salon. Special testing called "spore testing" is required to ensure autoclaves are working properly and this testing should be done monthly, or more often. These are special packets that are put through a normal autoclave cycle and then sent to a laboratory for testing to ensure it is in good working order. Regular maintenance is required to ensure the autoclave is capable of properly sterilizing implements. Autoclaves become ineffective if not working properly, so they must be tested regularly, as described in more detail in a question 10:1 below.

In short, proper disinfection is required in salons, while sterilization is optional.

Just remember, whatever you decide to do, do it right and always exactly follow manufacturer's directions.

### 1:  Myth If I use a hand sanitizer, do I still need to wash my hands?

Hand sanitizers do not replace hand washing because they cannot remove dirt, grease or other debris from the skin or nails. For this reason hand washing with liquid soap and warm running water is the preferred method. However, the use of a hand sanitizer following proper hand washing, can add an extra measure of protection. If used more than 10 times per day, they can dry the skin so be sure to use a high quality hand moisturizer at least once per day.

### 10:1 You said in an earlier episode that autoclaves need maintenance and testing to verify they're working properly. Can you give us more information about how this is best done?

In the US, the Centers for Disease Control (CDC) recommend weekly testing of autoclaves to ensure that they are properly sterilizing implements. Other countries have similar rules or recommendations. Maintenance is relatively easy. The autoclaves owner manual provides information about regular maintenance requirements, e.g. cleaning, replace seals, etc. Contact the manufacturer for more information about repairs and maintenance. Don't be misled by the color-changing indicator strips on autoclave bags. These are only an "indicator" and don't assure you that the autoclave is working properly. In fact, these strips can fool nail professionals. Of course, if they fail to properly change colors this will tell you the autoclave is not properly functioning. However, these indicators can give false results and will change color even if the proper and required pressures were not reached.

Achieving the correct pressure is just as important as the temperature; again indicator strips only detect temperature, not pressure. Regular maintenance is also required to ensure the autoclave gets to proper temperatures and pressure. Follow the manufacturer's schedule for: cleaning, changing the water, service visits, replacement parts, etc. The only way to ensure the autoclave is working properly is to do regular "spore testing". What is a spore? A spore is like a seed for fungal or bacterial organisms. Normally, spores do not cause infections in salons, but they are a concern in hospital surgical wards where they can cause infections. Even so, spore testing is useful for determining if an autoclave is working properly. You can purchase a sealed packet of specially prepared spores designed to be run through a complete autoclave cycle. This packet is then sent to a laboratory for testing. If the autoclave is functioning correctly, the spores will be killed 100%. If any survive, the autoclave is malfunctioning. You can search the Internet for a source to purchase these spore test kits and a lab to have them tested. Or you can ask the manufacturer of the autoclave, they should be able to provide this info. Web search for "autoclave spore testing."

I recommend performing a spore test at least once per month. If these tests are not performed regularly, then the salon cannot claim to be properly protecting their clients. In fact, they may be putting their clients at risk. Hospitals perform these tests weekly, but salons are not at all like hospitals and the risks of infections are thousands of times greater for hospitals, so monthly is probably fine for the salon setting. Many companies offer plans for monthly testing that are surprisingly low in cost. If you have an autoclave, I recommend signing up for at least the monthly plan. If you're using the autoclave constantly, then you might want to sign up for weekly testing. You don't want your autoclave malfunctioning for weeks or months without your knowledge. This is the only way to make sure that your autoclave is working properly. Also, each time you perform a spore test my recommendation is to record this in a logbook along with other records related to cleaning, disinfection and maintenance of your autoclave and other equipment

**11:8 I ask all my clients to wash their hands before a service, but the lead technician in our salon says that causes lifting. I don't have any lifting problems, so am I right to do this?**

If the nail plate is immersed in water for more than 60 seconds, enough water could absorb into the nail plate in some cases (e.g. damaged nails), to make a significant difference in the water content of the nail plate. Even so, regular hand washing is NOT likely to significantly add water to the nail plate. Studies demonstrate that many never wash their hands for more than 5-10 seconds, but health authorities recommend 20 seconds. I recommend asking clients to carefully and thoroughly clean their nails with a clean and disinfected nail brush, before sitting down at the nail table. You never know what clients will bring to your nail station if you aren't careful. This is one way infections can occur and spread to other clients. Hand washing before a service begins is a great way to prevent infections.

**18:1 Could you please outline the best way to clean and disinfect nail files that aren't made of metal, glass or fiberglass. I've been told that porous nail files can't be disinfected and know some people dispose of them after each use which gets expensive! I bet there are countless technicians around the world using these and not doing it properly! A spray of a sanitizer for tools and implements may not be the best? What do you think?**

First, you need to know some background information in order to correctly understand my answer. So that we are speaking the same language, I must point out that "sanitizers" are like "cleaners" that don't disinfect. In fact, many sanitizers don't even clean a surface!

This word is mostly misunderstood and misused, which is why I do NOT recommend using this term.

Disinfectants are highly effective at killing bacteria and fungi on pre-cleaned surfaces, which some refer to as a "sanitized surface". In this case, the surfaces we're talking about are the parts of the abrasive that touch the client's nail plate. Every country has a department that approves and controls disinfectants and how there are used. In the US, the Environmental Protection Agency or EPA must approve the sale of any disinfectant products and they must also approve claims these products are allowed to make.

Those claims must be proven using approved tests or the EPA will reject the claims. Developing a new type of test and getting it approved costs more than hundreds of thousand dollars, so rather than do this, most companies take the more cost effective route and rely on existing test methods. This is what has happened with nail files. Several EPA approved testing protocols exist for hard surfaces, which helps explain why there are many different disinfectants that are approved for use on hard surfaces in salons. These disinfectants can be used on metal, glass or fiberglass backed nail files and drill bits as well. There are no approved tests for porous surfaces that can be used for nail abrasives and no one wants to pay all that money to develop an approved test for porous nail files. Though not only because of the high costs. Once such a test was developed, the approved test method could be used by anyone, so it would offer no competitive advantage to the company that paid to have the testing approved.

What's the consequence? There is no approved test that would apply to porous nail files. Although porous files are likely to be disinfected, no EPA registered disinfectant is allowed to make this claim. I once chaired a task force for the California Board of Barbering and Cosmetology that looked into the disinfecting of nail files. Our task force research included discussion with the EPA who told us that porous nail files could be disinfected, but until a protocol was developed they would not allow EPA registered disinfectant to claim to be useful on porous nail files.

Furthermore, it is illegal to use an EPA registered disinfectant unless it is used exactly as directed on the label and for the specific purposes for which it was designed. US State Boards of Cosmetology can't permit EPA registered disinfectants to be used on porous nail files, even though they would likely work. Our task forces recommended to California that they allow 10% bleach solutions or 70% Isopropyl alcohol as disinfectants for porous nail files since they are considered to be effective disinfectants BEFORE there was an EPA. They didn't need EPA registration to be used as a disinfectant. To make these effective, the file would first have to be washed clean to remove all visible signs of debris.

Disinfectants don't work so well on dirty surfaces; they are designed to work best on pre-cleaned surfaces. Once the file is clean, it can now be completely submerged in the 10% bleach solution (90% water) OR 70% isopropyl alcohol for ten minutes. After which the disinfected file should be thoroughly rinsed in clean running water, allowed to dry in a dust-free location and stored in a clean, dry covered location that is not sealed. The reason for not sealing is to allow any moisture to escape. Wet implements are a breeding ground for bacteria and fungi. The reason for covering them is to keep dusts off implements. Bacteria and fungi can't jump, run or fly, but they sure get around. How? The answer is by "touch", they are transferred by direct contact such as touching, or using a contaminated nail file. We also know droplets of a sneeze can carry them as well. For bacteria and fungi, dust particles are like magic carpets that can take them just about anywhere the air is moving. So dust must be kept off clean and disinfected nail implement and files. Which helps explain why it is NOT wise to file a VISIBLY infected nail plate. The dust can carry large amounts of bacteria or fungi into the air.

Normally, inhaling bacteria and/or fungal organisms isn't a problem since our bodies have defense mechanisms that swiftly deal with these invaders. However, filing upon an active infection can release a lot of contaminated dusts. Active infections typically produce visible coloration or other changes in appearance within the nail plate, e.g. crumbling into pieces. Such nail plates should not be serviced and should not be filed. If this is done inadvertently, I recommend that the nail file should be sealed in a disposable bag and thrown into the trash.

You should know that if the nail file falls apart during cleaning and disinfection, it is not a reusable nail file and should be disposed of into the trash. It is also very important to know that spraying a disinfectant doesn't make it work any faster. Most salon disinfectants work in ten minutes, some in three or five minutes, however none work in seconds. Spraying alcohol or other disinfectants on a nail file does virtually nothing to protect the client. The file MUST be washed first. If a sprayer is used to deliver the disinfectant, the nail file or other implement MUST remain wet with the disinfectant solution for the time specified on the disinfectant label, e.g. ten minutes. When in doubt, be sure you are exactly following the label's directions and you can be certain to use the disinfectant properly. Also, I mentioned drill bits in the list of things to disinfect. Yes, drill bits must be cleaned and disinfected between clients, not just dropped in acetone. Acetone is not a disinfectant.

**26:1 One of my clients is really afraid of bacteria and is becoming more afraid all the time. She heard on TV that everything is covered with bacteria, so now she washes her hands twenty times a day and it's having a horrible effect on her skin and nails. What can I tell her so that she won't be so afraid and stop having nail services? She questions everything I do now and I'm a stickler about cleaning and disinfection.**

The news media tends to exaggerate these risks and overly frightens the public. In the last ten years many have become overly afraid of bacteria and this frightens many potential clients away from salons, since they perceive there is a big danger. The same is true for fungi, which many refer to as "fungus". Even their mention causes many to worry. Here are the facts. Most bacteria and fungi are not only harmless, they are very beneficial. Very few of them are "pathogens" which means that very few types can cause infections in humans. Many of those that can become infectious, only do so under unusual circumstances.

The "microbiota" is the term used to describe normally occurring microorganisms that live in and on our bodies. In fact there are more microorganisms in the human body than there are cells. There are about 10 trillion human cells in our bodies and according to recent and more accurate measurements, we know there are also about 10 trillion microorganisms in and on our bodies. Knowing this makes it seems kind of silly to be so afraid of them, especially when they do so much good for us and keep us healthy. There are about five hundred species of microorganisms in our bodies, about fifty different species account for the majority of them. These microorganisms live in harmony with us and assist the body in many ways. For instance microorganisms breakdown sugars, carbohydrates, fiber and many other nutrients so we can digest them. Without these microorganisms, we could not efficiently process these much needed substances and would eventually starve to death.

Microorganisms also help make our immune systems stronger and work better; they keep the more potentially harmful microorganisms under control so they don't become overpopulated. Most of those that are infectious are "opportunistic" organisms. This means they are normally harmless. They only become harmful when the immune system fails to work properly, or due to side-effects of drugs or medications, over fatigue, malnutrition, or as a result of injury. In other words, when an opportunity develops, a few microorganisms can take advantage of the situation to grow and thrive. For example, if the skin is cut or abraded, this allows normally harmless bacteria to get past the skin's natural defensive barrier to gain access to tissues where these microorganisms normally don't live. They DON'T burrow or just absorb into the skin to cause infections. That's important to know. Without the normal controls to keep their populations in check, when some bacteria get into damaged skin they can get out of control and may grow to unusually large numbers to cause infections. Most of these infections by pathogens can be prevented by eating well, getting plenty of rest and avoiding injury to the skin. The skin is a natural barrier between us and the outside world. The skin is designed to keep us healthy and to protect us from nature.

Nature is a dangerous place. We don't live in nature anymore, so we tend forget how dangerous it can be. Pathogens are natural! Nail salons have some great methods to help protect us from these inherent natural dangers. What we call cleaning and disinfection is an important form of "infection control". These are important ways to help eliminate the "opportunities" for infection. These procedures help by preventing pathogens from reaching potentially dangerous levels, keeping their populations well below concentrations were they could become harmful. Proper cleaning and disinfection reduces the levels of potentially harmful pathogens by 99.99%. This tremendously reduces the risks of infections to the skin or nails. This is another way to prevent cuts, abrasions or other damage to skin while performing salon services. When these practices are done, the risks of infection drop even closer to "zero".

What increases the risks for clients? One way to put clients at greater risk is for a nail professional to ignore their responsibility to properly clean and disinfect between each client, every time! Another way to increase risks is to play "doctor" and attempt to treat clients that have an active nail or skin infection. Nail infections are medical issues, not cosmetic issues. In many countries, only trained medical professionals are allowed treat infections on other people as a part of a paid service. When nail professionals attempt to treat these problems in the salon, they prevent clients from getting proper diagnosis and treatment. Also, they run the risks of spreading the infection to other clients, which could ruin the reputation of the salon. My advice to this nail professional was to continue to be a stickler about cleaning and disinfection, and to be proud of it. All nail professionals should make sure they are adhering to the proper cleaning and disinfection procedures. Never cut living skin and don't perform services on clients with any type of infection, always refer them to a medical professional for proper care and treatment. Let your clients know that this is how you do business and they'll keep coming to you, trusting that they are in good hands.

## 32:4 If we use good sanitizing procedure how close are we to 100% clean and is this something compared to sterilization with an autoclave?

Few things are 100% clean. Clean dishes are typically about 98-99% "clean". We don't disinfect or sterilize dishes, since there is no need. Sanitizing is reducing the amount of bacteria, viruses and fungi to the levels considered safe by health care standards. In this case, 99% is considered very good. Some sanitizers are cleaning agents, some don't even clean. None are disinfectants. This is a commonly misused term in the salon industry which is why I avoid the use of the words "sanitize" or "sanitizer". These words are mostly used incorrectly; therefore, I use the word "clean" instead. Properly cleaning salon implements, probably removes 99% of contaminates on a surface and when this is followed by proper disinfection, these implements will be 99.99% or more free of debris and infectious organisms. Sterilization does not clean at all, which is why only pre-cleaned implements should be sterilized. Proper sterilization would kill 100% of the pathogens on a surface, so the difference between disinfection and sterilization is about 0.01%. The question then would be is this 0.01% considered a problem in salons? In my opinion: No.

Hospitals regularly rely on disinfection to prevent the spread of pathogens. Sterilization is only considered necessary when performing surgical procedures, entering the body cavity or other unusual circumstances. So disinfection is considered by health care professionals to be a powerful form of protection. That's why more things are disinfected in hospitals than those that are sterilized. It's very fortunate that proper disinfection works so well. Many items in both hospitals and salons cannot be sterilized, so relying on proper disinfection is critical. Table tops, arm rests, pedicure basins, floors, counters, door knobs, and telephone receivers are but a few examples. Even so, cleaning, disinfection and sterilization all must be done properly or the surfaces may remain contaminated.

## 32:5 How important is it to use the correct ratios when mixing disinfectant solutions and will too much or too little water not properly clean implements? Also, do ultrasonic devices help any with a better clean-up of implements?

It is important to exactly mix the proper amount of disinfectant solution to water or the solution will not be as effective. This means it must be properly measured, not estimated and not measured by "eye". Either too much or too little water can lower the effectiveness of a disinfectant. The amount of water to be added to a salon disinfectant is determined by extensive testing. Different amounts of water are tested to determine the exact amount of water needed to achieve the maximum effectiveness. No, more is NOT better! Making a stronger disinfectant solution doesn't make it more powerful, in fact this can lower the effectiveness of that solution.

Common isopropyl alcohol is a classic example. Using 70% alcohol is far more effective than 99% alcohol. Also, making a disinfection solution too strong or too weak can make the solution more likely to dull or rust implements. Pitting and corrosion can make pedicure basins and other implements more difficult to clean and allow pathogens a place to hide from disinfectant solutions and thereby lowering their effectiveness. Ultrasonic cleaners use high frequency sound waves to enhance the effectiveness of cleaning solutions. Ultrasonic devices can help ensure that implements are clean before they are disinfected or sterilized, however these devices should not be used to replace cleaning with a scrub brush, liquid soap and running water. After proper cleaning, an ultrasonic cleaner for example may dislodge debris that could be hidden in a pivot point of a nipper where a brush could not reach, so they have some usefulness. They are not needed to make disinfectants work and I've not seen any evidence that they make disinfectants work any better.

## 37:3 Why do metal implements rust and is the rust dangerous?

Rust is a common concern, since many people grew up hearing stories about how a rusty nail or other pieces of rusty metals can cause infections such as tetanus. That is a myth... rust does NOT cause tetanus or any other type of infection. Tetanus is caused by a bacterial infection. If these bacteria get deep into the skin, this can lead to a very serious infection. But this can just as easily happen with a rust-free nail, and some are infected with these bacteria by puncture wounds from thorns on plants such as rose bushes. Even so, rust is NOT a pathogen and rust is NOT toxic. What is rust? The word itself is comes from the German word for "red". About 1200 BC iron began to replace bronze for the making of tools and weapons. The Roman historian and philosopher Pliny the Elder hypothesized that the Gods had created rust to limit the destructive power of iron weapons... which we know now is a rather silly notion. That's not surprising since the ancients had made lots of silly notions and didn't have much understanding of the world around them.

Rust is caused by water and oxygen working together to oxidize iron into iron oxide. Rust is a type of iron oxide. Water is the main culprit that causes this oxidation process. Other metals can also oxidize. Copper and bronze, for instance, will form colored patinas on their surface because of oxidation. When iron rusts, the rust takes up more space or volume which causes expansion. As this expansion continues, the metal begins to separate into layers and flake away from the surface.

This creates pitting and more flaking which leads to more rust formation of freshly exposed metal surfaces in contact with water and oxygen. This leads to the corrosion that is typically seen when metal rusts. Since steel is made mostly of iron, it is no surprise that steel implements are corroded by rust when exposed to water and oxygen, unless proper care is taken. That's why it is important to completely dry all metal implements and keep them in a dry location. This will also prevent the growth of pathogens, since they require water to live and reproduce. Therefore, keeping metal implements clean and dry has many benefits.

**37:4 I use rubber-based silicone toe separators, not the porous type. Can these be sanitized and then disinfected adequately? Do you think these will deteriorate from liquid disinfectants over time? Can these be sterilized in an autoclave?**

Silicone is highly resistant to disinfectants. Toe separators can be cleaned and disinfected very easily and the silicone won't break down. Even highly porous toe separators can also be disinfected, but some regions have regulations against disinfecting porous items, even though being "porous" actually make it easier to disinfect, not harder. "Porosity" is a relative term and just about everything has some degree of porosity. In my view, the whole porous/non-porous discussion is actually just a big misunderstanding. I've not heard a rational reason why something porous can't be disinfected. Hospitals and nursing homes regularly disinfect bed sheets and reuse them.

Silicone toe separators are a good example, because they will not absorb disinfectants, so are they porous or non-porous? Most would say they are non-porous, but then how is this explained? When soaked in colored disinfectant solutions they will absorb and become stained by colorants in the disinfection solution. The silicone surface can become slightly blue, purple, red, yellow or even grayish. This coloration change indicates that the surface absorbed some of the disinfectant, demonstrating that the surface is actually slightly porous. This color change is just a cosmetic effect and won't affect the function of the toe separators. Even though silicone has some porosity, there is no doubt that these items can be properly disinfected. These can be repeatedly cleaned and disinfected for many years, so don't throw them away after a single use.

This is an interesting property of many types of silicone. They allow some molecules to penetrate their surface. These molecules are mostly restricted to near the surface. The nail plate can do the same, as I've discussed in previous questions. This is exactly how smokers get stains on their nail plates when they are repeatedly exposed to cigarette smoke. I've not tried, but I don't think silicone toe separators can be sterilized in an autoclave without destroying them. Autoclaves are very hard on anything not made of metal or glass. Even so, disinfection is clearly enough for silicone toe separators and will kill 99.99% of microbes on the surface, thus rendering them safe for reuse on clients.

## 40:4 My question is about UV light boxes that non-standard salons and hairdressers use for disinfection. Do these really work?

I understand what you mean, but I'd like to take this opportunity to remind everyone that UV is not light. Light is energy that your eyes can see, but UV is invisible so it is NOT light. Instead, UV it is a form of energy, so we should call it UV energy or simply UV, as I will do in this book.

Now to answer your question, these so-called "UV sanitation" devices will NOT properly clean, disinfect or sterilize implements. For those purposes they are useless and I do NOT recommend them. If you already have one and want to continue to use it, my recommendation is that it only be used to store previously clean and disinfected implements/tools. They make great dust-free storage cabinets, but that would be all I would use them for in the salon. So in my opinion, the UV devices sold to salons for implements are a waste of money. UV-C energy is used to sterilize devices, but UV nail lamps do not produce any UV-C, at all. Instead, these devices reply on UV-A which has a much lower ability to kill pathogens. Another big problem is that the UV energy can't reach both sides of the implement nor can the UV get into tight spots, e.g. pivot points on shears. This is why the US Environmental Protection Agency (EPA) and other agencies in other countries recommend full emersion of these implements/tools into a liquid disinfectant to prevent the spread of pathogens.

# Product/Service Quality and Safety

## *Section 6*

### 5:1 What do you recommend is the ideal temperature and humidity for a salon?

It is ideal for salons to maintain a steady, comfortable temperature and humidity. Avoid wide swings in temperature- which can affect products. A good ideal range is between 68-78°F (20-23°C). It is comfortable working conditions and comfortable for clients, as well. Lower than 65°F (18°C) begins to affect cure and/or dry times, as does higher than 80°F. Cooler temperatures help improve products shelf-life and higher temperatures can shorten the useable life of products. Relative humidity (RH) is the measure of amount of water vapor in the air. 40-45% RH is generally considered comfortable in the temperature ranges mentioned above. Lower temperature and RH are less suitable for growth of common fungi and bacteria in the salon. 50-60% RH is considered average comfortable zone. Above 50%-60% RH and air begins to feel increasingly moist and higher than 70% RH promotes growth of fungi and bacteria. Dehumidifiers can be used, however, be sure to empty, clean and disinfect them regularly, as directed by the manufacturer. I recommend that salons empty and clean humidifiers daily and then clean and disinfect them weekly.

### 5: Nail Myth: Nails need to Breath.

Sorry, no they don't and there is no evidence to support this silly notion. Here's why: the nail plate isn't alive and doesn't have any lungs nor do they have any ability to absorb air into the nail plate. Nails do not require an external air supply and do not breathe nor do they exhale. Also, 100% of the oxygen needed by the nail matrix comes from the blood stream and 0% comes from the outside world. Everything the nail plate needs to properly grow and function is delivered and removed by the blood. When the nail plate is coated with any nail coating, including nail polish, moisture and natural nail oils will pass through the nail plate at slower than normal rates, but they aren't "trapped". The nail plate's moisture content is increased by 10-15% and the natural oil content increases only slightly, e.g. 1-2%. Both oil and water in the nail plate serves to increase the flexibility of the natural nail plate.

Waste products are removed from the matrix and other tissues by the blood and are not released into the nail plate. Nail plates can grow and thrive in a completely air-free environment. All they need is a healthy flow of blood to the nail matrix, bed and surrounding tissue.

Clearly, nails don't need to breathe for any reason. Those who say differently just don't understand how the nails grow or function. Some marketers use such claims to fool nail technicians into thinking their products are better because they allow the nail to "breath", but they don't provide any evidence that this is useful. Claims that this improves the condition of the nails or prevents infections are unproven and in my view are false and misleading claims, until proven otherwise. I don't recommend letting such claims influence your purchasing decisions.

## 10:4 What about applying nail enhancements to children under 16? I've been told that this is unsafe? Why?

I hear this question often and I generally reply in this way-wearing any type of nail coating is like owning a puppy. Mom and dad should be the ones to decide when their child or young adult is old enough to have either a puppy or nail coatings. Since I am unaware of any scientific or medical information that suggests there is some minimum age, I think it is best to rely on the parent's decision to determine the right age for this, or any other type of salon service. Different people reach the required maturity at different ages.

Puppies are a lot of fun to own and in a young person's mind, so are artificial nail coatings. However, just like puppies, nail coatings require responsible care, maintenance and upkeep expenses. This requires a certain level of maturity and commitment. I know 40 year olds that don't fit this requirement and should NOT be wearing enhancements, so who's to say a responsible teenager shouldn't wear them? Of course, your professional opinion should come into play as well. If you as a nail professional are ever uncomfortable with applying any type of artificial nail coatings to anyone for any reason, then don't do it.

**21:2 What is the safest and best way to switch a client from an enhancement to a UV gel manicure coating? Is it better to slowly grow out the enhancement or remove it properly and then apply the UV manicure coating? I feel like my client's nails look so weak and fragile after an enhancement removal, that I fear removal all together. So I grow out enhancements by gradually thinning the existing product and applying the UV manicure service. But then I get chipping and flaking.**

There is no need to remove an enhancement that's in good shape and generally it is successful to fill in the areas of new growth with the new nail coating product. Of course, if the enhancement is experiencing any substantial amounts of service breakdown, I'd recommend removing it and starting fresh with a new coating. UV gel manicure nail coatings are very different and are often designed for complete removal on a regular basis, e.g. twice per month. For this reason, I believe it is best to remove the nail enhancement coating before applying a UV gel manicure product. However, the more important question is: Why are your client's nails weak and fragile after removal?

This should not occur unless the client's nails were over-filed during application or the nail enhancement is removed improperly. Simply wearing a nail coating doesn't damage the nail. That is a big myth. Nail damage is most often a result of improper application and/or improper removal: not simply from wearing enhancements. Remember, artificial nails coatings are "enhancements" not replacements for the nail plate, so always perform your services in a manner that protects the condition and health of the nail plate. In other words, respect the nail plate. The nail plate's strength, condition and health should never be compromised by any type of nail coating. When properly applied and removed, any damage should be minimal to non-existent.

If the nail plate shows thinning after removal, that thinning was done by the nail file not the enhancement or UV gel manicure product. Some are fooled because while wearing an artificial nail coating, the water content of the natural nail plate can increase from 15% to 25%. When the nail enhancements are removed, this extra 10% of water will dramatically increase the flexibility of the plate. By the next day, the moisture content will return to normal and so will the nail's flexibility. Some nail professionals and clients will misinterpret this extra flexibility as "weakness". The nail isn't any weaker, just temporarily more flexible. Even so, if you determine that the client's nails are too weak or fragile for nail services, you should discontinue any nail service that may further thin or weaken the nail plate.

**21:3 I have one client who "believes" that soaking off her enhancements with her foiled finger in a plastic bag sitting in a bowl of warm water is less irritating for her skin than when the foil covered enhancement is placed under a 60w incandescent bulb. I'm worried that having the nails in a moist environment, rather than dry, while soaking is a bad idea. She claims her skin is itchy the next day when we place the foils under the warming glow of the bulb. The water method takes longer, leaks and is incredibly inefficient. I've suggested to her to use no heat, no water and no warming lamp, but she won't listen. I buff the top coat to break the seal, wrap with remover soaked in a cotton ball and wrap in tin foil. What do you think?**

In general, the addition of heat always makes a solvent more efficient, not less. Any nail solvent remover will work much faster when gently warmed. Of course it is important to warm solvents safely, especially if they are highly flammable, as acetone is known to be. Never heat a solvent to any warmer than "Jacuzzi temperature", 103°F or 40°C. There is no need to use "hot" solvent, since warm solvents will work very efficiently and will be a lot safer to work with in the salon setting. By more efficient, I mean the nail coating will dissolve faster. Why? For the same reason that warm water will dissolve sugar much faster than cold water. Water is the solvent in this case and warming it is expected to make it an even better solvent.

You need not worry about soaking in a moist environment since this should have no negative effects on soaking. Also, you may not realize this, but the removal method that you are presently using also relies on additional heat to speed up the removal process. The hand is pretty warm, about 98°F (36°C). The heat of the hand warms the acetone inside the foil wraps that you're using and will speed up removal. Even though you don't seem to care for the water method that you described, I think it is a very good idea if done properly. Acetone will be heated evenly, safely and very efficiently by the warm water method, which is why I recommend using this method over all other ways of warming solvents. Using the warm water to warm up the acetone is much safer, because it avoids using an electrical heat source near the highly flammable acetone. Acetone should never be warmed in a microwave or on a hot plate and not with an open flame or any electrical devices such as coffee cup warmer or blow dryers. Unless the electrical device is specifically designed to safely warm nail remover solvents, it should not be used for such purposes.

Floating a small plastic bottle partially filled with acetone and with a slightly loosened cap inside a bowl of warm water is a very safe way to gently and safely warm acetone. The warmer acetone becomes, the faster vapors are produced and the stronger the smell. With more vapors in the air, the acetone will be even more flammable, so be especially cautious to avoid any sources of open flame or sparks. You should not have incense burners, candles or other items in the salon which could ignite the acetone vapors. Nor should smoking be allowed in the area. Be sure to store acetone is a cool location and away from the heat of direct sunlight.

I'd also like to comment on your client's itchy skin. In this case, the itchy skin is probably a form of skin irritation or worse. Nail technicians should always be concerned when a client tells you that something is causing itching or you see other signs skin irritation such as redness, rash or unusual and long lasting warmth in those same areas. In fact, I recommend that you stop the procedure that causes the itching and use an alternative method until you determine the cause.

Skin allergy can begin with the same symptoms as simple skin irritation, so these can be difficult to tell apart. I'd recommend erring on the side of caution in this case and assume the client may be in the process of developing an allergic reaction. When a client complains of skin irritation, the last thing you want to do is dismiss their concerns and proceed as usual. This is a warning sign that should NOT be ignored. When clients tell you that their skin feels unusually warm or itchy in specific areas that could likely be a signal of an impending allergic reaction in that same area. Allergic reactions to nail products are almost always caused by prolonged and/or repeated skin contact with nail coating products that are supposed to be kept off the skin. These problems don't develop overnight and there are usually many warning signs, as previously described, so don't ignore them.

Any/all artificial nail coatings can cause adverse skin reactions, including UV gel manicures, however none of them would cause these problems if prolonged and/or repeated contact were avoided. Occasional accidental contact with the skin isn't what causes these issues. Irritation and allergy is most often caused by repeated contact. If repeated contact is always avoided, adverse skin reactions to nail products would be very rare.

Additionally, if a client's skin is itching while soaking their nails, this can be a sign that the nail coating is not properly cured! Properly cured nail coatings contain very little unreacted ingredients leftover to cause adverse skin reactions. However, when they are under-cured, nail coatings will contain excessive amounts of unreacted ingredients. These unreacted ingredients can escape from the nail coating into the acetone or other product removers to cause skin over-exposure to these unreacted ingredients. Some types of unreacted ingredients may cause skin allergies or irritation.

How can under-curing occur? Using the incorrect UV nail lamp or not changing the UV bulbs on a regular basis are common reasons. When nail technicians use the wrong polymer powder or use too much monomer liquid in the bead when using liquid and powder nail coatings, are two likely reasons for under cured enhancements of this type. Avoid both situations and make sure your nail coatings are properly cured.

## 23:2 Can you contaminate a bottle of polish by using it on someone with a nail fungus?

All professional salon nail polishes are designed to be applied to normal heathy nails and should not be applied to visibly infected nail plates. Nail polish should never be used to cover up an active nail infection of any type. Studies conducted by the Nail Manufacturers Council on Safety (NMC), which is a part of the Professional Beauty Association, demonstrated that nail polish does not harbor infectious bacteria or fungi when properly used. In other words, disease causing organisms, which are called pathogens, cannot live or grow inside nail polish. This includes fungi, bacteria and viruses. Why? There are three main reasons:

First, nail polish contains no water and all pathogens must have water to survive. Second, nail polish contains no nutrients or food that pathogens can use and like all living things, including pathogens; nutrients are required for growth and reproduction. Third, the solvents in the nail polish attack and break apart the pathogen's cell walls which kill them with amazing efficiency. The studies conducted by the Nail Manufacturers Council on Safety confirmed this and their study demonstrated that nail polish will not harbor pathogens and that nail polish aggressively kills common salon pathogens that could be accidentally introduced in to the polish. Which indicates that nail polish can be shared with other clients in the salon without concern. However, this is true for healthy nails that aren't visibly infected.

Here's an important word of caution. These study results may not apply when nail plates are visibly infected. Visible infections can contain tremendous amounts of bacteria or fungi. Thousands of times more than would ever be found on a natural nail plate with a healthy appearance. This means that visible infections are in a class of their own and should be carefully avoided. So to be on the safe side, any use of nail polish on visibly infected nail plates should also be avoided. In other words, if you accidentally brush over a visible infection, my own recommendation is the same as that of the Nail Manufacturers Council on Safety- out of an abundance of caution and keeping the client's protection in mind, the nail polish bottle should be properly discarded into the trash and not given to the client either.

### 25:1 How do you feel about the risk of cross contamination from dipping in paraffin wax?

About 12 years ago I spoke to someone who I consider to be a careful researcher and who had thoroughly examined this issue. His research revealed that bacteria and fungi are NOT at all likely to grow in these paraffin baths probably because the water content is so low that infectious organisms could not survive. He also theorized that the wax seals around the hand to prevent bacteria or fungal organisms from escaping into the wax.

This makes a lot of sense to me and I agree with his findings. Interestingly, there was only one case where this researcher found any infectious organisms in a paraffin bath. Understanding how this occurred is very interesting and important to know about. In this one case, the paraffin wax was badly contaminated and looked extremely cloudy. The cloudiness was due to large amounts of water and other contaminants in the wax. If water gets into paraffin, then some microorganisms may be able to survive. This was an extreme case of contamination, not what normally would ever occur. How did the paraffin become so cloudy and contaminated? The reason for this extreme contamination was the salon owner. That's right, the owner of the salon had instructed the nail technicians to "save the wax" after removal from the hands. It was then thrown into a container, and each morning, the previously used wax was then re-melted it into the paraffin bath as need just so the salon owner could save a little money.

Of course this is clearly improper to do, highly risky and certainly against the paraffin manufacturer's directions. This was a blatant misuse of the product! Only fresh wax should be put into a paraffin bath. All used wax must be disposed of after a single use, because paraffin wax is not reusable. After completing his testing, these researchers concluded that when a paraffin bath is regularly cleaned and all used wax is properly disposed of without reuse, it will be extremely unlikely for infectious organisms to survive and to cause infections. I'll add that if clients wash and dry their hands before the service, then the potential contamination becomes even less likely. These conclusions are also in complete agreement with other research that I've read on this subject. Other studies of paraffin collected from salon and tested for contamination of bacteria or fungi have found none of these. Therefore, this leads me to support the conclusions that dipping in a paraffin bath to perform salon services is a safe practice.

I would like to add a word of caution. Common sense dictates that client's with open sores or visible signs of an infection should not have these services. The researcher I spoke about did not suggest this as a concern, however I'm adding this warning to remind salon professionals that they should not perform services on any client with a visible infection of the skin or nails.

## 29:3 I'd like more information about breaking systems. We all know not to break systems but even I've done it without harm. So, how far does the term "system" stretch? For instance, adding other brands pigments or glitters or nail foils?

Any company would like you to apply their nail polish to their enhancement products and to use their nail oil or hand lotion but these aren't the systems I'm concerned about. I'm talking about matched pairs of products that are designed to be used together in order to function properly and safely. Good examples are monomer liquid and powder or UV gels and nail lamps. Even primers, removers and nail prep products are often formulated and tested to ensure they work well together and are compatible. This question that was asked really isn't about breaking systems; it is actually about following directions.

Adding something to a nail powder or UV gel that wasn't designed for that product may mean you're using it incorrectly. The nail professional is skipping all the testing a manufacturer would normally do to ensure an additive is safe and effective. Just because nothing happens when this is done, doesn't mean much. I can close my eyes for 30 seconds while driving. Just because I don't have an accident, doesn't mean that driving with my eyes closed is safe or wise. Often there are long term consequences related something a nail professional started doing a year ago. For instance, some clients may take many months or even years to develop an allergic reaction. Small changes may affect only small percentage of clients, causing them to have service breakdown. Often nail professionals blame such problems on something the client is doing. Many times it's related to something they changed months ago.

When product lines are mixed together and not used as they were designed, unexpected consequences can occur. Don't expect some kind of warning, instead understand that you've created a situation where something unexpected and surprising may eventually happen. This could put you and your clients at increased risk for something to go wrong. It may not happen today, maybe not tomorrow, but maybe in month or a few years. Perhaps it will be a combination of several changes over time that will trigger unexpected problems. This isn't just speculation, I've seen this happen many times.

When the issue occurs, the nail professional has no idea how to solve the problem because it is related to many things they are doing and not just one. Here is an example: a nail professional may decide to mix a pigment into her UV gel and doesn't notice any problems over the next month. A few months later, she buys some nail foils at a trade show and still doesn't notice any problems. She reads on the Internet about a new UV base gel someone is raving about, so she tries it. Then she buys a different UV nail lamp that's on sale, when the old one wears out. Six months later, she notices that several of her client's nails are breaking more easily and she's doing more repairs than ever before. A few clients develop oddly discolored nail plates and several are becoming sensitive, the skin around their nails is red and swollen or the nail bed is feeling tight or itchy. What's going on and how can she solve these problems? Many struggle with such problems all the time and don't ever solve them. These things happen all the time and I get questions like this on a weekly basis. Over the years I've noticed that nail professionals rarely think it is something they are doing, most blame the products or the clients.

Anyone who's ever educated for a nail company or worked their company's Educational Hotline can tell you a hundred stories like this. It might be something the client is doing or a defective product, but in my experience, most often it's something the nail technician is doing/not doing. Skin reactions usually occur because nail professionals make up their own directions, mixing different product lines together, creating their own blends or improperly applying, curing or removing the nail coatings. I understand that nail professionals consider themselves artists and want to be creative, but painting a canvas or sculpting in wood is not the same as working on someone's nails and skin.

Many have left the industry because they couldn't keep clients and many ex-clients tell their friends to avoid artificial nail coatings because of all the problems they've experienced. Until nail professionals become more educated about these issues and begin to follow directions more carefully, these problems will continue to plague the nail industry. My hope is that you will help solve this problem by educating yourself and others about the importance of using professional nail products properly and safely.

**33:1 When it gets really hot in the salon, which is most of the time, I can't stand the smell anymore and I always have a headache. I want to improve my ventilation. What do I do? I want something that's going to work.**

Too many nail salons don't pay proper attention to ventilation, even though this is an important part of working safely. There are a range of things that can be done to improve the quality of your salon's breathing air. The goal of all nail professionals should be to minimize inhalation exposure to potentially irritating or harmful substances. Problems can develop when nail professionals don't take steps to avoid excessive inhalation of dusts or vapors. Taking the right steps will improve the salon environment for customers and create a safer, more pleasant workplace for salon professionals. This is especially helpful for sensitive individuals. They can develop irritated eyes, nose or throat, headaches, difficulty breathing, nervousness or drowsiness. Each of these can be related to poor ventilation or ventilation that's not appropriate for the services being performed in the salon. Drowsiness at work might seem like it would not be related to poor ventilation, but it can be. We normally exhale carbon dioxide with every breath. When salon ventilation is poor, carbon dioxide levels can build up in the salon. This can make you feel tired and listless. Excessive carbon dioxide in the air can even lower your performance and negatively affect your decision making skills. Poor ventilation allows product vapors and dusts to accumulate, as well.

Just about every substance on Earth has both a safe and potentially unsafe level of exposure. Salon vapors and dusts are no exception. In properly ventilated salons, vapors and dusts are well within safe limits. Not all salons have proper ventilation. Some don't understand the importance or they may not understand the correct steps to take or even where to begin. Some may be confused by misinformation about salon ventilation.

For instance, a common myth is that the safety of a nail product depends on how it smells. It is a mistake to believe that ventilation systems are solely for controlling strong odors. Odors are not the reason for ventilating and the odor of a substance does not indicate whether it is safe or harmful. Dirty socks and baby diapers may not smell very good, but they aren't harmful to breath nor are their odors dangerous. Fragrances smell wonderful, yet some people are sensitive to inhaling excessive amounts. Some vapors have very little odor, yet they should also be controlled and kept at safe levels. That's why it is important to have a good understanding of these issues and how to keep vapors and dusts under control and within safe levels. Minimizing inhalation exposure is an important way to ensure that nail salon products are properly and safely handled and over exposure is avoided.

What is Product Overexposure? Nearly every substance on Earth has both a safe and potentially unsafe level of exposure. Injury may result if these safe levels are exceeded repeatedly or for prolonged periods. Don't ventilate to control odors; ventilate to control vapors and dusts, that's a great way to help avoid overexposure. It is especially important to control the air quality of your breathing zone. Everyone has a breathing zone; it's an invisible sphere in front of your mouth that is about the size of a beach ball. Every breath you take comes from this zone. Using proper ventilation helps ensure the breathing zone is a source of high-quality air. To achieve this goal you should first focus on having a properly maintained HVAC system.

An HVAC system is the built-in, general salon ventilation and air-conditioning systems. HVAC stands for "Heating, Ventilation and Air-Conditioning". HVAC system is designed to exchange air inside the salon with fresh air from the outside and to remove dusts and pollens. These are highly effective at capturing dusts and removing vapors when outfitted with replaceable activated carbon and "electrostatic" dust filtering panels. These absorbent filtering panels eventually become saturated, making them ineffective, and therefore must be replaced three to four times per year.

All HVAC ventilation systems must be properly maintained and cleaned on a regular basis so it is best to work with a local HVAC specialist. These skilled professionals can diagnose the salon's air quality and ventilation systems and provide useful solutions and advice that will keep the system working at its peak capacity. Next you should focus on protecting your breathing zone by using a source capture ventilation system. These systems are designed to capture vapors and dust particles right at the source and then extract them from the breathing zone. Once the vapors and dust are captured, they should be passed through a multi-stage filtration system. This system should have HEPA filter, which are pre-filters designed to remove dusts. Some activated charcoal air cleaner devices utilize a dust pre-filter that is machine washable or replaceable. The system should have a separate, second stage filter that contains a minimum of 2 lbs. (1 kg) of activated carbon. Typically, such a filter will be at least 2 inches thick (5 cm). The thicker the activated carbon bed, the more vapors will be removed. Thicker is better and will last longer before needing to be replaced.

The opposite is also true, if these filters are too thin, they are practically useless. My advice is to avoid any ventilation systems with little or no activated carbon e.g. those with flimsy carbon filters less than a ½ thick or 1.25 centimeters. Why? The vapors pass through the filter much too quickly to be absorbed and the majority of the vapors are just blown back into the salon. These types of devices work like a fans, they merely blow the vapors away to other parts of the salon. This does reduce the odor at the nail table but that's not the goal; cleaning the salon air and removing vapors and dusts is the goal.

Devices with thin carbon filters aren't ventilation; they are a form of "circulation". These devices fool many into thinking the vapors are being absorbed, when they are not. They are just redistributing the vapors in the salon so everyone can breathe them equally. I don't recommend wasting your money on an ineffective ventilation system. Using a ventilation device that doesn't work well is like putting a screen door on a submarine. What good is it doing other than giving you a false sense of security? When properly designed and correctly used, source capture systems protect the salon air and the breathing zone and are the most effective way to prevent excessive inhalation of dusts and/or vapors. Source capture systems that return filtered air into the salon can work very well if properly maintained, e.g. filters changed as directed.

Even so, when practical, always directly ventilate air to the outside. If you can do this, it will be less expensive in the long run since you won't need to purchase replacement air filters. Secondly, I recommend also using a "professional" HEPA room air cleaner, but not as a replacement for source capture system. Instead a stand-alone salon HEPA room air cleaner can be an extra step to help further clean the salon's air. Avoid air cleaners designed for "home use". They remove pollen, cigarette smoke, etc. and are not suitable for salon use. Use a professional quality air cleaner designed for salons that utilize HEPA filters and a thick carbon bed.

I don't recommend using ANY air cleaners that produce even tiny amounts of ozone, even as in the parts-per-billion (ppb) concentration range. This is done to "neutralize odors", but doesn't remove vapors or dusts. Ozone is a hazardous air contaminant, even at very low concentrations. The Environmental Protection Agency (EPA) has warned all consumers against using air cleaners that release ozone due to the health risks they create. These devices sometimes cause watery eyes, runny nose, coughing, chest tightness, metallic tastes in the mouth, shortness of breath, and blurred vision. These are not effective for controlling dusts or vapors in salons. Both healthy people and those with respiratory difficulty can have breathing problems when exposed to even relatively low levels of ozone, for example more than 40 parts-per-billion (ppb). Other helpful tips are; use trash cans with a self-closing lid and place one at every work table. Empty trash cans several times per day and change liners daily. Properly ventilate storage area where professional products are kept. Keep all product containers tightly closed when not in use. Perform all salon work in a well-ventilated area.

One of my many responsibilities as Co-Chair of the Nail Manufacturer's Council on Safety (NMC) is to work with other nail industry scientists and experts to create informational brochures that help nail professionals understand how to work more safely with professional nail products. Recently, I worked with a team of NMC and ventilation industry experts to create a significant new update to an existing NMC brochure. The brochure is titled "Guidelines for Controlling and Minimizing Inhalation Exposure to Nail Products". The brochure is printed in English, Spanish, Korean and Vietnamese. Read this useful brochure for free at www.probeauty.org/NMC. Give yourself the peace of mind that comes with having the right information. You'll make wiser choices if you do.

### 33:2 The mask I use doesn't seem to be helping and I end up tasting dust in my mouth after I file. What mask do you recommend?

Filing can create a lot of dusts that ends up in the breathing zone of the salon worker. Disposable dust masks can be used to minimize inhalation of dusts, but these are not effective for vapors. Those that claim to be effective for vapors are for home use applications and not suitable for salon uses. Dust masks are good at preventing inhalation of dust particles, but they are not good at absorbing vapors- because they are too thin!

Dust masks should never be used in place of proper ventilation. Even so, when properly used, the correct mask can be an important way to prevent inhalation of excessive amounts of dust particles. They are especially useful to those with pre-existing asthma, allergies, or other breathing related conditions. The best disposable masks have an "N95" rating and are the most effective for salon workers. These are thicker than most masks and better able to block 95% of the fine particles that attempt to penetrate the mask. For any dust mask to work well it must fit well. Better quality dust masks will fit and seal more securely and comfortably and do a better job overall. Dispose of these masks regularly and follow the manufacturer's directions for use. Avoid using surgical/doctor-type masks since these will not provide enough protection and should not be used in the salon setting. Doctor-type masks may help prevent the spread of germs, but are not suitable for salon work.

### 30:1 What are Hindu Stone manicures and are they safe? They look similar to pedicure stones. How are they similar or different?

These so-called Hindu stones have been sold to nail professionals under various names for many years and are nothing new. These are made of pumice, which is finely ground lava rock. These manicure stones are very similar to the stones used in some nail salons to remove calluses. Lava stones are used mainly because they are highly aggressive and remove calluses quickly. The main difference between the different types of lava stones are the size and depth of the holes in their surfaces.

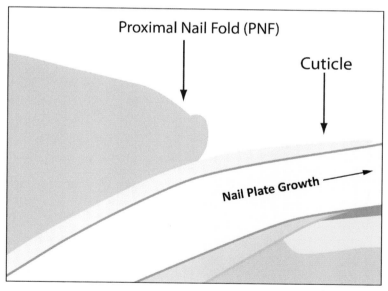

For use on feet—the holes are very large and deep, and for manicuring—they are very small and shallow. Pumice stones have been prohibited in many places mainly because they can be very difficult to clean, especially the stones used for pedicures. The large holes quickly and easily trap dead tissue. The holes make these stones very difficult to properly clean, since skin is hard to remove from the deep crevices. If they can't be properly cleaned, then they can't be properly disinfected. I personally don't recommend these be used on feet. These stones are too aggressive and often used to completely remove calluses. As explained in other questions, calluses should only be smoothed and should never be completely removed. Complete removal of a callus makes the foot more susceptible to injury, blisters and infection. Calluses are designed to protect the feet.

Pumice stones used for manicuring have very small surface holes that are not deep, so these are much less likely to trap debris and therefore are much easier to clean. I have not tested them to determine if they can be properly disinfected, but I suspect that they can be disinfected if they are carefully cleaned. This means removal of all visible signs of debris before being completely immersed a disinfectant. The biggest problem in my view is that for manicuring, these stones are very hard, highly abrasive and not flexible. This causes them to be overly aggressive and damaging to the natural nail plate. To make matters worse, they are sometimes used to remove the very thin cuticle tissue adhering to the thinnest and softest part of the nail plate. What? Or I should ask why? Isn't this like using a chain saw to mow the grass? You can do that, but why would you want to? This is extreme overkill and these pumice stones are not the best way to safely and carefully remove cuticle tissue.

If excessive downward pressure is used with these stones, the nail plate may be seriously damaged and overly thinned. Instead, I recommend using a disposable wooden pusher stick, which is much safer. Metal curettes are also very useful for this purpose, but metal pushers can be too sharp and may injure the living tissue. Regardless of the implement used, I recommend a using a soft touch whenever working on the nail plate and especially near the lunula (moon) where the nail plate is softest and not yet fully hardened. Nail damage to this area occurs easily so take appropriate care.

**39:2 I've been looking at SDS's and comparing UV gel polishes. How do I tell if it's a good one or not? What should I look out for exactly? And... what should I steer clear of? What would be the UV gel polish with the best case scenario ingredients?**

I'm glad you are using these very important information sheets. Every salon should have them for every product they use in the salon. For those that don't know, SDS stands for Safety Data Sheet (aka MSDS). These information sheets are used around the world by many different types of professionals, include fire fighters, truckers, shippers, packagers, etc. The SDS teaches important information about safe use.

For instance, they provide emergency contact phone numbers, first aid information, proper storage, flammability warnings, safety precautions, proper disposal information and even provide signs to watch out for which may indicate the products are being improperly used. They also provide signs and symptoms, if any, for both short-term and long-term overexposure. You won't be able to tell a good UV gel from a poor one by reading these safety data sheets. Why? That's not what these data sheets are designed to do. The SDS tells you what you need to know to work safely with the product and doesn't consider product quality or performance. All brand name nail products can be used safely when they are used correctly. By correctly, I mean that all manufacturers' directions are followed and all warnings or precautions are heeded, including those listed on the safety data sheet.

To answer the rest of the question, I don't think there is such a thing as "best scenario ingredients". It's not that simple to tell how well a UV gel will work, especially given that if a nail professional misuses the very best UV gel in the world, it won't work very well. Many will blame the product, when in fact they used the product incorrectly. That's one of the biggest challenges facing the nail industry. Too many nail technicians don't read or follow directions and they mix together things that should not be mixed; many technicians incorrectly cure nail coatings. Of course the reverse is true; a great nail tech can make even a poor quality UV gel work pretty well. These safety data sheets and the ingredient listing can warn you about ingredients that you may be allergic too so you can avoid exposure, so that's another way they are useful.

I did want add something else. It used to be that we read the labels to find out what's in the products. Many people read the labels to find out what's NOT in the product. That doesn't make a lot of sense. Unless you are allergic, what does it matter what isn't in the products? Labels often contain cleverly spun marketing messages. For instance, "this product is XYZ-free!" This claim is very often used to fool people. A good example is acetone-free. So what if the product is acetone-free? Acetone doesn't cause allergic reactions and it can easily be used safely in salons. Acetone-free doesn't tell you what's in the products. Maybe the solvent used to replace acetone isn't as safe as acetone. When people see the XYZ-Free claim, they automatically assume that XYZ must be dangerous. That's a clever ploy that many fear-based marketers use to fool people into thinking their products are safer, when in fact they may be no safer... and may even be less safe.

"Three-free" is another example and now some are claiming to have "ten-free" nail polishes. They often don't even bother mentioning what they are supposedly free from and they don't need to bother. They know this claim will frighten many into buying their products, regardless of what they don't contain. My advice is this, don't buy a product based on what it doesn't contain. Don't let fear drive your buying decisions and be very wary of marketers that use fear to sell their products. Buy from companies that provide fact-based information, not fear. Good nail products don't need to be marketed with fear. Good marketers don't need to stoop to these types of deceptive practices. Be informed and make informed purchases. Read the safety data sheets and use the products properly. That's the best way to ensure you are working safely.

# Service Breakdown/Filing/Prep

## Section 7

### 3: Special Topic "Breaking Systems: What is it and what's wrong with it?"

Professionally applied artificial nail coatings are often designed to be part of a system. Sometimes, two (or more) products are designed to be a "match pair", e.g. part A and part B.

Monomer liquids and polymer powder (aka Liquid and Powder) are a good example of a matched pair. Another great example are UV nail lamps and UV cured nail coatings. These are matched pairs designed to be used together. In my opinion, when someone tries to sell you a nail lamp and they don't make a UV gel- they are just trying to sell their UV lamps and don't really care if they properly cure your nail coating or not. Nor do they have any way of ensuring the lamp will properly cure the coating product.

Only the manufacturer of the UV gel can tell you which lamp works with their UV gel product. Never use LED-style UV nail lamps to cure UV gels that were designed for use with the fluorescent style UV nail lamps. Various UV gels contain different photoinitiators (PI) that cure the UV gel. Some contain complex combinations of these PI. Different products can have a wide range of different PIs in different combinations. Different blends of ingredients will cure differently when exposed to UV energy, which is why UV products cure differently and they are NOT all the same.

For many reasons, the manufacturers of the UV gels are the only ones who can provide directions for proper curing of their nail coating products. They are required to ensure the products they sell are safe when used as directed and all warnings or precautions are heeded. Only the UV gel manufacturer can tell you which nail lamps you should use and their directions should be followed. All precautionary statements understood and heeded. The manufacturer is responsible for providing information about safe use of their product and it is the nail technician's responsibility to heed this information.

Liquids and powders (aka monomer liquids and polymer powder) are designed to work as a matched set. The monomer is the key to these systems, not the powder. The powders are important, as well, and the performance of the monomer liquid depends on using the correct polymer powder and at the proper liquid to powder ratio; medium dry, never wet, never runny. There is no such thing as a "universal powder". When the incorrect powder is used with a monomer liquid, the resulting blend will have an increased change of being improperly cured, which is a leading cause of adverse skin reactions. Prolonged and/or repeated skin contact with improperly cured dusts, filings or sticky roll-off can cause skin irritation or permanent skin allergies that worsen with continued exposure.

When it comes to matched pairs, these are some reasons why they are important to use properly. Don't be fooled by misinformation and don't become allergic to the tools of your trade.

## 2:1 When nail oil is applied directly to a fresh nail enhancement will it cause lifting?

When the enhancement is properly applied nail oils will not cause lifting. Here's why. Nail coatings form a tight seal with the nail plate and nail oils cannot get underneath. The benefit of nail oil comes from the natural oils that penetrate into the nail enhancement to increase plate flexibility and durability. Applied daily they can maintain the flexibility of the nail coatings and enhancements. High quality nail oils can also condition the surrounding living tissue.

If there is pre-existing lifting or any separation between the coating and the nail plate, nail oils can cause the lifting to increase. They may wick underneath the coating to soften and weaken the adhesive bonds holding the coating to the nail plate. If lifting increases while using nail oils, that doesn't mean you should discontinue use their use. Instead, it would be wise to reexamine your techniques to ensure you're proper cleansing and preparing the natural nail surface and properly curing. These are much more likely reasons for lifting.

## 2:2 Can medications cause artificial nails to lose adhesion and lift.

Normally, these are not likely to cause these problems and here's why. Doctors often state that the health of the natural nail is a window into the health of the individual, so some suspect medications are causing problems with adhesion. Most likely, taking medication for a month or two isn't going to affect adhesion of artificial nails or coatings to the nail plates. Same is true for over-the-counter (OTC) medications, which are typically taken only for a few weeks. There are certain medications that when taken for long periods that can affect the way the body functions and may affect nail growth. However, this is would be uncommon for medications, in general.

An example of medications that do affect nail plate growth are chemotherapy drugs, since they can halt growth. Anesthetic given during surgery is sometimes blamed for nail problems such as lifting, but I've seen no evidence to support this. People are often leery of medication of any type and tend to jump to this conclusion quickly when they see problems with their nails. It is far more likely that medications would affect nail growth, than nail coating adhesion. Nail technicians should not suspect medications for causing lifting until all other potential sources of the problem have been investigated and ruled out. Medications are rarely the cause of artificial nail adhesion loss and it more likely caused by something the client is doing, e.g. a sudden lifestyle change. Also, if a person is taking a lot of medications and their nails are in poor condition, it is more likely that the condition of the nail plate is due to poor health of the body, and not the medications. For instance, those taking heart medication may also have blood pressure and circulation problems and these health issues are far more likely to adversely affect the condition of new nail growth, than would the medications themselves.

## 2: Myth: "The prenatal vitamins are why women's nails grow like crazy!"

Wrong, with or without prenatal vitamins, women's nail growth accelerates during pregnancy. The highest recorded rate of nail growth is during the last month of pregnancy. After delivery of the baby, nail growth rates almost immediately return to normal- even if prenatal vitamins are continued to be taken after the birth. Vitamins can't make your nails grow faster than just eating healthy. If you don't eat healthy, vitamins certainly will not make your nails grow any faster. Save your money and use high quality nail oils. You'll be better off. In my opinion, supplements that claim to accelerate nail growth are making misleading and deceptive claims.

## 14:1 How does the grit of abrasive affect the natural nail? Are there grits that shouldn't be used on the natural nail and why? I've been told to not use any coarser than a 180 grit on natural nails but I don't know if this is supported by science.

The "grit" describes the average size of the abrasive particles. The lower the grit number, the bigger the abrasive particles on the file. A 60 grit particle is a little more than three times larger than a 180 grit and five times larger than a 240 grit abrasive particle. That may not sound like much difference, but if you are 5 feet tall, someone five times larger would be 25 feet tall. It's like comparing a Volkswagen with a two story house. A good rule to remember is the lower the grit, the bigger the abrasive particle, the deeper and wider the scratch it will leave in the nail plate.

120 Grit

In my opinion, the natural nail can be properly prepared using a 240 grit, if the nail plate is properly cleaned and prepared. This requires removing oils, debris and dead cuticle tissue from the nail plate's surface, since these can block adhesion of all nail coatings. Problems develop when the nail plates are not properly cleaned and carefully prepared. This is one reason why I recommend that clients wash their hands with a clean and disinfected nail brush BEFORE the service begins to remove surface oils as well as bacterial and fungal organisms. Rather than take the time to properly prepare the nail plate, some chose to do their nail prep work with a 180 grit file which will remove surface oils along with a few of the upper layers of the nail plate. It can result in excessive thinning of the nail plate. This is especially more likely if proper care isn't taken and too much downward force is applied.

Anything lower than 180 grit is risky business when used on the natural nail plate and is very likely to lead to excessive damage. In my view, the only reason for using grits lower than 180 is to reduce thickness of the existing nail coatings for quicker solvent removal. Reducing the coating thickness decreases soaking time, but this should be done cautiously to avoid damage to the underlying nail plate and bed.

*(images show nail plate surface after being filed or "buffed" with the respective grits)*

**18:2 I explain to my clients the importance of home maintenance, use of a high quality nail oil, etc. and I even give each client written home maintenance and a free nail oil, but they just don't do it and continually have service breakdown because of the nail plate and product being too dry. If you have any ideas to share about how you would encourage client cooperation I would love to hear them!**

Often when nail professionals say the enhancement is too "dry", they really mean too brittle. Too "dry" would mean that the coating contained too little water, since dry is the opposite of wet, but these coatings do NOT contain water. Saying enhancements are too dry isn't very descriptive and misses the point, it can prevent a proper understanding of the real causes of the issue- the nails are too brittle and not because they lack moisture. Nail oils don't add moisture to reduce dryness, that's not how they work. Instead, they reverse the brittleness of the nail coating by absorbing into the plate to increase flexibility. They allow the nail's layers to slide past each other more easily. Since the real problem is brittleness, a good solution is to reverse brittleness with a nail oil.

When it comes to the product, my advice is to first ensure the correct application techniques are in use. Review the product's application instructions to ensure that you're not deviating from the proper procedures. If you are, this should be the first thing you suspect is the reason for the nail coating brittleness.

If problems continue and you are sure everything is correct, talk to the client about their lifestyle. Are they doing something that is increasing brittleness, not wearing gloves when cleaning, excessive hand washing, and overuse of hand sanitizer, etc. Some clients wash their hands dozens of times a day, which is too much and can lead to nail brittleness and skin irritation. Providing proper information is the best way to ensure clients are adhering to their home maintenance. Explain to them the best way to prevent nail enhancements from becoming brittle is with regular use of high quality nail oil. They work much like a leather conditioner prevents brittleness in leather. Explain that what they do with their hands is out of your control and you provide them with nail oil to keep the enhancements in top shape. Explain that your extra repair work with every appointment costs you time and materials and that you will have to charge extra for these. If they are still unwilling to properly maintain their nails, then I would indeed charge them for the extra repair time or I'd fire them as a client. Wearing artificial nail coatings requires proper maintenance and those who refuse to properly maintain their nail coatings should not wear them. A tip for encouraging the use of nail oils is to tell the client that while they are watching their favorite TV shows each night, to use the time to apply the nail oil and massage them into the nail and surrounding skin. Reminders like this may help them remember, if their checkbook doesn't. Any client that does NOT take the responsibility to properly maintain their enhancements is bound to cost you time and money making unnecessary repairs.

## 36:2 My understanding is some L/P systems are porous, but gel is not. Top coats that don't have a dispersement layer are non-porous and do not soak off. Is this correct?

No, it is not correct. All nail coatings are porous, just to different degrees. In fact, no type of artificial nail coating ever created is completely "non-porous". For this reason, we should only talk about the porosity of a nail coating when compared to other nail coatings. For instance, UV gels tend to be less affected by acetone when compared to two-part monomer liquid and polymer powder systems. Both types of enhancements are less affected by acetone than fiberglass wraps or nail glues. Nail polish is the most affected by acetone; therefore it is the easiest to remove. The ease of removal is also in the same order of porosity; UV gels are the least porous and nail polishes the most porous, at least toward acetone. The more porous the nail coating is to acetone is the easier it is to remove. Therefore, UV gel is less porous to acetone than liquid/powder which is less porous than wraps. In this way porosity helps determine the rate of penetration by acetone.

The natural nail is many hundreds of times more porous to water than to nail oils, due to its size and chemical makeup. Artificial nails are porous to many solvents and ingredients in nail oils. All nail coatings are all porous to both of these, but to different degrees. A general rule to remember is that the more porous the nail coating is to acetone, the more porous it will be to nail oils, as well. The reverse is also true. So, nail oils are more likely to penetrate Liquid and Powder nail coatings than they are to penetrate UV gels. Nail polish is the most likely nail coating to be penetrated by nail oils.

"Dispersement layer" is not the correct term to use. Most likely you are talking about the "inhibition layer" which is caused by oxygen inhibition of the surface cure. I discussed this in more detail in question 25:2. Oxygen at the surface prevents proper polymerization and that's what is responsible for these sticky layers. Porosity depends mostly on the chemical composition of the cured nail coating and how well the nail coating is cured. Over-cured nail coatings will have a lower porosity, while under-cured nail coatings have a much higher porosity. This explains why it is harder to remove a nail coating that has been over-cured. Under-cured leads to greater porosity, which is why under-cured nail coatings stain more easily. Their surfaces are more porous and can allow stains to accumulate under the surface to cause discoloration.

## 40:2 I am spending a lot of time rebalancing gel nails by way of manual filing, sometimes spending an hour if I take over another nail tech's client. How do you feel about electric filing?

I believe that electric nail files have a place in the nail industry, when they are properly used. However, just because you can buy an electric file, doesn't mean you know how to use it correctly and safely. To do so requires knowledge, practice and skill which doesn't come with the purchase of a new electric nail file. A lack of these three things often leads to the use of e-files in an unsafe manner and may result in serious nail damage and/or injury. For this reason, I don't recommend their use on the natural nail. I realize that some possess a great degree of skill and claim to never over thin the nail plate. They are far from the norm and their use is potentially risky for the client's natural nail plates. Over filing the natural nail is one of the biggest problems facing the nail industry.

Over filing the nail plate is already too easy with a manual file. The risks of nail plate damage greatly increase when electric files are used. The reason for filing the nail plate isn't to remove multiple layers, instead it is to increase the surface area so that the nail coating has more to grab and hold on to in order increase adhesion. Increasing the surface area of the top few layers will provide the same adhesion benefits as stripping away ten layers. So, if the adhesion levels are the same, why strip away ten layers of the natural nail? There is no reason for doing this, other than a lack of knowledge and/or lack of attention. This misguided practice is a left over from the early days in the nail industry when many incorrect practices were taught, still exist today, and are continued by some nail educators. To use any nail file safely requires knowledge, practice and skill, it also requires care and attention to the client's nails.

Because of the potential for nail plate damage, my recommendation is to NEVER use on a client until after the nail professional gets training from another nail professional who possesses the necessary knowledge and skill. In short, if used carefully and properly, electric nail files can be used safely, but they can create serious injury and significant damage when improperly used, so they should be avoided unless the nail professional obtains specialized training in correct use.

### 40:3 Why do some products not require filing of the nails? The fingernail is oily and we were always taught to remove the gloss. Why do some product applications not require this?

You are correct, it is important to remove the gloss or shine, as some call it. The gloss is from surface oil and the nail plate with no surface oil appears dull. If the goal is to remove the "shine", that's just the surface oils, but this is not what generally happens in salons. The surface nail cells are NOT glossy and they don't shine. This glossy appearance is caused by the natural oils that coat the surface of the nail plate. Only the natural oils need to be removed, not the surface of the nail plate, which only needs to be lightly buffed on the surface. Washing the hands and scrubbing the nails with a disinfected nail brush is the best way to remove surface oils. This two-step process will ensure that all surface oils are cleansed from the nail plate and the surface is finely scratched without thinning the nail plate.

The nail file is needed to slightly increase the surface area, which improves adhesion. Here's how that helps: lightly buffing the nail plate's surface dramatically increases the surface area as microscopic scratches on the surface expose additional nail plate surface for the nail coating to hold on too. Almost none of the thickness of the nail plate needs to be removed to increase the surface area and improve adhesion, yet some nail technicians remove 5% or more of the nail plate's thickness each time they file.

More filing just thins and weakens the nail plate, this doesn't improve adhesion. It fact, over thinning the nail plate will lower adhesion! The nail plate becomes highly flexible, each time the nail bends, this puts strain on the interface where the nail coating and natural nail meet and bond. This extra strain weakens the adhesive bond and leads to increased lifting and peeling. Newer formulations of nail coatings have very good adhesion and require much less filing, yet many nail professionals continue to regularly over file the nail plate.

It's easy to see the effects of over filing, when the nail coating is removed. The area of new growth should not be much thicker than the nail plate that's been filed and covered with a nail coating. All of the lost nail plate thickness is due to filing and NONE is due to the nail product itself. Yet, many clients see this thinning and incorrectly believe the nail coating "ate the nail", which of course is silly. No nail product can eat or thin the nail plate, except a nail abrasive, e.g. electric file. So in short, I recommend you remove as little of the nail plate as possible. To keep the nail plate strong, it must be kept near its natural thickness. In other words, please, keep the nail plate thick.

### 13:3 Does filing the sides of the natural nail really weaken the free-edge? I've been given this myth as a reason for using the square shape too many times, so I had to ask!

This is a myth. It doesn't make any sense that filing the sidewalls would weaken the free-edge, but I do agree that square shaped nails are more likely to break than those that are rounded. What causes this? A rounded free edge doesn't have a corner that can break off and a square nail has two corners that can break or chip. The square corners increase the potential that the nail will be snagged on something and break off. Also, an oval shape is inherently more resistant to certain types of breakage. That's why Romans invented the arch, to support their bridges. Arches more evenly distribute the weight, as well as other forces such as sudden impact. The force of impact would be better distributed by a rounded shape than one that that was square. Keep in mind that the lower arch of the nail must also be kept intact for strength, not sacrificed for the shape when choosing a non-square option.

### 16:4 Are glass nail files really better for natural nails?

What's better for the nail plate is to use nail files that are not overly aggressive. Low grit abrasives are more likely to shred the nail plate, which can lead to over thinning and peeling at the free edge. Glass files are equivalent to high grit abrasive and are therefore less damaging, unless used overly aggressively. How the file is used is important too! Excessive downward pressure can still damage the nail plate, even when less aggressive files are used. Downward pressure multiplies the effectiveness and therefore the aggressiveness of any nail file, so use caution. Pressing down less is best!

## 16:3 Does filing in only one direction, towards the center, really help the nail?

I have not found this to be true and I've tested this concept by using high magnification photography to record the results of various filing techniques. After examining nail plates filed using various abrasive grits and filing techniques. I didn't observe any differences in the condition of the plate when comparing filing in only one direction with filing in a back and forth fashion. This study was conducted on normal, healthy nail plates, so perhaps there may be a difference if the nail plates are damaged, but this appears to be a myth. I've seen nothing to support the claim that filing in only one direction provides any benefits.

## 16:2 I understand that acetone and other prep products dehydrate the nail plate only temporarily and that nail oils counteract the effect quite well. Does nail polish or UV gel polish dehydrate the nail at all?

Acetone only dehydrates the surface of the nail plate, and these nail coatings do the exact opposite for the natural nail, they hydrate. Every nail coating from nail polish to UV gels will temporarily block passage of water at the upper surface of the nail plate, causing higher levels of moisture to build up underneath the coating. This increases the water content of the nail plate from typical 15% water up to 25% water when coated with an enhancement or natural nail overlay.

Nail oils work in a similar fashion. These oils contain NO water, so they cannot add moisture to the nail plate. Instead, the oils slow down the passage of water moving from the nail bed upward to the surface of the nail plate, which increases the nail plate moisture content. The same thing occurs when anything covers the nail plate, including artificial nails of all types.

**16:6 I have a question about metal cuticle pushers – I would like to know how dangerous it is to use a metal pusher vs a rubber pusher with cuticle remover. I'm really slow with a rubber pusher and cuticle remover, since I am as thorough as possible. I want good adhesion, but I am concerned about how much damage pushers could cause. Is it OK to use a metal pusher if you're super careful and gentle or should they be avoided entirely?**

Implements used to remove dead cuticle tissue from the nail plate can be made from metal, rubber or wood. Any of these can be used without creating damage and any of these can create damage when used too aggressively. So, each of them should be used with care and caution. I don't think "pushers" is the right name. They should not be used for pushing the proximal nail fold, which is the proper name for the living tissue at the base of the nail plate. This living skin is part of a protective seal that prevents infections of the matrix and surrounding tissues.

You are correct to be concerned about damaging the lunula area where the nail plate is the thinnest and softest. I also agree that it is important to remove all of this dead tissue in order to ensure good adhesion, as long as the proper precautions are used. Any type of cuticle remover can be used safely when properly applied. However, one downside to the removers with an alkaline pH is that they can be difficult to remove completely from the skin. When not completely removed, residues can irritate and even severely damage living tissue.

Another approach is to use a high quality nail oil to soften this thin layer so that it can be gently removed. Of course, any residuals of these oils must be cleaned from the nail plate; or the removers themselves can block adhesion of nail coatings.

## 14:4 I'm not sure about pH or what pH balancer products do. Is it necessary to use one, along with a dehydrator with some or all nail coatings?

If you understand pH, it will make many other important concepts much easier to understand. The pH is a measure of the acidity or alkalinity of water. Water normally isn't acid or alkaline; it's exactly in the middle at the neutral point. Some people use the word "basic" instead of "alkaline", but these terms are identical.

One of the most important things to understand is that only water can have a pH, nothing else. No exceptions. Only water, which includes the water found in water-containing products. Nothing else can have pH. For instance, nail oil does not have a pH because it contains no water, but if you mix the oil with water to make a lotion, the lotion will have a pH, which will be the pH of the water in the mixture. Dissolving other substances into water can change the water's pH to become more acid or more alkaline, depending on what's added.

Interestingly, when you measure pH, you measure how much acid or alkaline substance is dissolved into the water at that moment. For example, if I blow bubbles into water, the water will change from "neutral" to "acidic" because the carbon dioxide in my breath will be dissolved into the water and make carbonic acid. The pH can be used to measure precisely how much acid or alkaline material is dissolved in the water phase, which is why pH is an important measure of quality for lotions, creams and other water containing cosmetics. When a product is made incorrectly, the pH will often be different. Most manufacturers will specify the allowable pH range for a product and may reject a batch if the pH is wrong.

The nail plate contains water, but the pH of the nail is difficult to determine. It is known that the pH of the water inside the nail plate can be temporarily altered if exposed to acidic or alkaline substances. Vinegar for example is acidic, so if the nails are soaked in vinegar, it is expected that the pH of the nail plate will become more acidic. The same would be true if the nail plate were soaked in an alkaline baking soda solution; the plates would become more alkaline. As the pH of the water in the nail changes, this causes a slight change in physical shape of the proteins inside the nail plate as they adjust to the new pH of the water in which they are submersed. There can also be some minor chemical changes on the surface of the nail plate that are related to pH.

These changes alone are small, however combined they can produce a minor improvement in surface adhesion. Altering the pH won't make a huge difference, but it can help a little. The idea behind a pH balancer is to temporarily alter the pH of the nail plate, ideally making it likely to improve adhesion. Eventually, the nail plate will be restored back its normal pH. This is a temporary effect lasting hours, not days. When should you use such products? If the manufacturer of the nail coating system instructs the use of a pH balance, then this should be adhered to and I recommend that you carefully follow those instructions. In that case, the pH balancer is being used as a step in a "system" that is designed to ensure improved adhesion to the nail plate. So not following this step could adversely affect your final results.

My answer is completely different in the case of using a pH balancer that was not specifically designed for use with that nail coating product. If that pH balancer isn't recommended by the manufacturer, you should call them to make sure they aren't concerned about some unforeseen issues you may not have considered. I'd recommend caution. My recommendation is to listen to the nail coating manufacturer and follow their directions. They're the ones that can give you the best information about how to best use their products.

**35:4 "I keep seeing posts stating, 'the client has oily nail plates, that's why acrylic and gel polish doesn't last." My understanding is the nail bed doesn't have oil glands so this isn't possible. Clients can have creams or oils on their hands if they have not been washed correctly and the main reasons for gels and acrylics lifting is incorrect prep, not using correct ratios, mixing products or not using the correct lamp. Can you give me the correct scientific answer please?**

Yes, you are mostly correct. I do disagree with one thing, it's a myth that a lack of sebaceous oil glands in the nail bed means the nail plate can't contain oil. The nail bed and underlying tissues also produce natural oils of differing compositions than the sebaceous glands, but these other tissues don't make nearly as much oil as the sebaceous glands. About 3-5% of the weight of a nail plate is due to natural oils. Hair can contain twice as much. I do agree with you that if the surface of the nail plate is properly cleaned and prepared, that nail coatings will stick well to even normally "oily nail plates". Of course, very oily or wet nail plates can be a challenge, but these challenges can be overcome when the proper procedures/techniques are used.

Don't look for excuses for why the nail coatings don't stick, instead, examine your own work carefully. Many of these problems are more likely related to improper preparation, improper application, improper cure and/or improper removal. Examine each of these areas. Sloppy or incorrectly performed procedures may work ok for most clients, but these same procedures are more likely to cause problems with clients that have oily or wet nail plates.

# Working Safely/Avoid Skin Problems

## Section 8

### 4: Special Topic "Improving Salon Air Quality"

What can you do to improve the quality of breathing air in the salon? First you must understand what the salon requires. Salons should have proper and appropriate ventilation with the goal of ensuring a consistent supply of good quality air. Proper ventilation means to use the correct equipment (properly installed) and to ensure the equipment that is chosen is effective in the professional salon setting, always turned on during business hours and and kept well maintained, year round. Professional ventilation systems are the best option and systems specifically designed for nail salons are widely sold. I recommend investing money in a well-designed professional ventilation system.

Avoid using any air cleaner or other ventilation equipment designed for home use. Home ventilation units won't adequately protect your health and fool you into believing you have proper ventilation. Ventilation must also be "appropriate" for the salon's use, meaning that it fits the type of work/tasks performed in the salon and is effective even when the salon is full and all the nail technicians are performing their various services at the same time.

There is much more to know about ventilation than I can discuss here, but here are some tips to determine if a salon's existing ventilation system is "proper and appropriate".

1. Do strong product odors linger for more than 10 minutes after discontinuing use?

2. Can you smell odors from other rooms?

3. Are product odors noticeable when the salon is first opened in the morning?

4. Do clients complain or joke about strong smells or offensive odors?

5. Do you ever have to open a window or door because the odors are too strong?

6. Do the walls ever "sweat" with moisture?

7. Do the windows become foggy?

8. Are walls, furniture or floors coated with a thin layer of fine dusts?

Yes to any one of these? I recommend contacting a local expert on building heating, ventilation or air-conditioning (HVAC) and ask for an inspection. HVAC experts can be found locally or on the Internet. These specialists can check your salons ventilation for problems. They can also provide yearly maintenance and cleaning that will reduce air-borne dusts, molds, and pollens in your salon air, which can trigger inhalation allergies. They too are air contaminants that need to be controlled in the salon. Good salon air quality makes clients feel better about being in the salon and helps to ensure the nail technician's safety.

Salon owners should consider improving ventilation if anyone working in the salon experiences frequent headaches, nausea, sore throats, coughing, blurry vision or watery eyes. If this occurs, consult with an HVAC expert for solutions. Proper ventilation should eliminate "sensory irritation", e.g. burning or watery eyes or scratchy/irritated throat. I have not mentioned ventilation as a way to eliminate "bad" odors in the salon because the odor of a substance does not indicate whether it is safe or harmful. Dirty socks and baby diapers are good examples. They smell really bad, but these vapors are considered safe to inhale. Consider this, fragrances smell the very best, yet many are sensitive to their vapors. Don't ventilate to control odors; ventilate to control vapors and dusts, whether they are odorless or not. Short-term inhalation of dusts is fine, but avoid long-term, excessive exposure to ALL dusts. Any kind of dust can be harmful if excessive amounts are inhaled repeatedly for prolonged periods, e.g. three to five hours a day or more, three to five days per week or more. Don't just "neutralize" odors, that doesn't improve safety at all. Don't be impressed by claims of odor removal. Odors aren't harmful; they are helpful by warning that ventilation is inadequate. Don't ignore odors. They will be removed when you improve ventilation. Many vapors don't have a strong, distinctive odor.

Fumes are not what salons are trying to remove either. Fumes are a mixture of vapor and soot-like particle created from burning of a material. Car's burn gasoline and emit fumes. Welding and fireplaces create fumes. Burning candles and incense emit fumes. However, when liquids evaporate they emit vapors and not fumes. So when solvents, monomers, or UV gel products evaporate in the salon, they emit vapors - not fumes. I recommend to avoid using fans, since these only circulate vapors and dust around the salon for everyone to breathe.

It's far better to work in a manner that that minimizes vapors and dust formation. For instance, empty the salon's trashcans several times a day and use metal trash cans with self-closing lids, for better safety and vapor control. Also, use electric file nail oil when filing to reduce the amounts of dust in the air. These nail oils are especially designed to work with e-files and this is a highly effective way to significantly reduce the amount of fine dusts in the salon air. I highly recommended using them.

The most effective type of salon ventilation captures vapors and dusts at the source where they are created, the nail table. These systems are called source capture exhaust systems. When this type of ventilation is used together with general building ventilation, the combination is highly effective and significantly improves salon air quality. Source capture systems protect the "breathing zone", an invisible sphere that sticks out about two feet in front of the mouth. That's where all the breathing air comes from, so it's important to protect the breathing zone.

Dusts masks that bear an "N95" rating are considered to be high efficiency dust masks that filter out 95% of the particles in the air. These can be purchased on the internet. Only wear masks that are specifically designed for dusts. Doctor's masks or a painter's mask are not useful in the salon setting and will not protect the health of nail professionals. It's important to wear high quality dust masks to prevent inhalation of dusts. They can protect the breathing zone by removing most of the dust particles. Dust masks are not effective at blocking vapors from being inhaled, so never rely on a dust mask as a replacement for source capture ventilation.

Should clients wear dust masks? If they specifically ask to wear one that's fine, but they are not necessary because clients are exposed to less dust that most nail technicians are in their day of salon work. Clients will never be overexposed to inhalation in the salon setting. They are there too infrequently.

A standalone room cleaner should only be used in conjunction with source capture ventilation and with the general building ventilation. Never rely on room air cleaners to do the entire job alone. These can't protect the breathing zone and will only capture vapors and dusts after they escape from the table area into the general salon air. There are three zone or areas that need to be protected in salons; the breathing zone, the immediate area around the nail table and the general salon/building air. All three should be considered in order to ensure good quality breathing air for nail professionals and clients. However, none of them will work alone. Don't rely on just one of these. You can find more information about improving salon air quality by reading a free brochure "Guidelines for Controlling and Minimizing Inhalation Exposure to Nail Products" found at www.Probeauty.org/NMC. This is a valuable guide that's updated regularly and provides useful information to help improve your salon's air quality.

**15:2 As a nail professional I use professional products, but I would like to know a couple things about the DIY kits on the market. First of all, knowing how sloppy many people are when painting their own nails, aren't home gel polish kits an overexposure reaction waiting to happen? It's my theory that in the next couple of years we are going to see an upswing in people allergic to enhancement products. What are your thoughts?**

You could be right, but I sure hope not. The salon industry could also be tainted by negative PR related to improper home use of such products. Personally, I agree that professional nail products should not be used by untrained non-professionals. I also agree that these types of products can lead to adverse skin reactions, if they are not used correctly and skin contact is not avoided. Some clients are more likely to develop adverse skin reactions than others, so it's always best to assume that any client may develop skin sensitivity. Therefore, skin contact should always be avoided. Also, nail coatings should be properly cured, which further reduces the potential for skin reactions. When properly cured, nail enhancements are not likely to cause adverse skin reactions of any type. Too many clients do develop skin sensitivities because nail professionals do not take care to avoid skin contact and many do not properly cure the coatings. How many clients develop skin reactions? No one can say for certain.

Adverse skin reactions are an important issue that I will be talking about in many upcoming episodes. However, most, if not all, of these adverse skin reactions are completely avoidable. In other words, the reactions reported are almost always due to incorrect application and/or improper cure. For instance, some adverse hair bleach reactions result from improper mixing of two part hair bleaches or incorrect application, which is usually the result of not following manufacturer's directions or not heeding warnings. I've served as an expert witness in many court cases over the last twenty years. Several cases I've seen have involved scalp burns. Scalp burns can happen for other reasons as well, but several happen because a stylist accidentally mixed two parts of the powdered bleach with one part of the liquid activator, instead of following the directions which call for one part powder bleach and two parts liquid activator. In other words, they switched the concentrations and used twice as much powdered bleach as they should have used. This type of mixing error may cause some hair bleaches to heat to over 150F (65C), which can foam and leak from the foils to burn the thin tissue on the scalp.

Many nail professionals appear to be just as likely to overexpose the skin as are the do-it-yourself crowd. I've watched nail professionals work for many years and I've seen some pay virtually no attention to avoiding skin contact. The skin around their client's nails are red and inflamed. This type of visible irritation is very likely an early warning sign of a skin problem in development, or maybe a permanent allergic skin reaction. Permanent allergic skin reactions aren't what they sound like, but it's not a good thing either. Rashes and signs of visible irritation often appear to "go away" after the exposure is discontinued, but if exposure to the allergy causing substance resumes, the symptoms may worsen and return.

During my long career, only once do I recall a similar situation in which a retail nail coating product cause a significant increase in adverse skin reactions. This occurred when one of the first UV gel companies in the US began selling their products directly to consumers via a multi-level marketing scheme. UV gel kits were sold by consumers directly to other consumers and with virtually no training. These kits were even being sold at local fairs and street markets. The product's application instructions were very poor and there were virtually no warnings or precautions on the packaging. Users received far too little information and were not warned to avoid skin contact. To make matters worse, the UV lamp was very poorly designed and my testing showed that the nail lamp significantly under-cured the product on the nail. Here is why that matters:

Nail products harden when they exceed 50% cure, but they should be cured to about 90%. I measured the degree of cure for this retail product and believe it was about a 60% cure. It then slowly cured over the next 16 weeks, but barely achieved 70% cure. This means that the users were exposed to improperly cured dusts/filings, which can be a source of some skin reactions when long term, repeated skin exposure occurs. Within six months after the commercial release of this product, users began to develop skin itching, redness and other complaints. After a little more than a year, this nail company went out of business, which was not a surprise, given the problems they were having. Education is the key. Information is the best way to ensure proper and safe use. When the right information is used wisely, nail techs can avoid issues related to irritation or allergy. Of course, this will also depend on how well the instructions and warnings are written, as well as, how well the UV lamp is designed by the manufacturer.

Hopefully, those selling such products will learn from these mistakes and not repeat them, e.g. using an ineffective UV nail lamp to cure the coating. My biggest concern, a company developing a retail nail lamp that was improperly designed and did not properly cure the nail coating. This could likely lead to excessive adverse skin reactions. Unfortunately, not enough understand the important role that UV nail lamps play and why ensuring proper cure of the nail coating is an important part of safe use.

## 20:2 What are the proper precautions to take if you cut a client?

Any cuts, abrasions or breaks in the skin can create exposure risks to visible blood or body fluids. These should be assumed to contain infections organisms from which you must protect yourself and clients from exposure. I'll generally refer to these organisms as "pathogens". Some typical examples of pathogens are the flu and cold virus or hepatitis B virus. However, of these three, only hepatitis B is a pathogen transmitted from person to person by direct contact with infected blood or body fluids. These types of pathogens are called "blood borne pathogens". When it comes to blood borne pathogens, you should err on the side of caution whenever there is a potential for exposure to cuts, abrasions, wounds, bruises, etc.

There are several standards that make recommendations designed to protect against transmission of pathogens. One that you should be aware of is called the "Standard Precautions", which are written and published by the US Center for Disease Control (CDC). You can read more about Standard Precautions on many Internet health-related sites; I'll outline how to use to precautions when an exposure occurs in nail salons. In this case, an exposure means blood or fluids draining from a cut, wound or abrasion. Once exposure occurs, the recommended precautions are to immediately stop the service and after apologizing to the client:

1. Put on a fresh pair of disposable gloves, I recommend nitrile or vinyl gloves.

2. Apply gentle but firm pressure to the area with cotton to stop the bleeding.

3. Apply an antiseptic to the area.

4. Apply an adhesive bandage to completely cover the wound.

5. Clean and disinfect your workstation using a disinfectant approved for salon use.

6. Dispose of all throw-away items such as table towels, contaminated nail files and cotton balls into a plastic trash bag and seal the plastic bag completely closed before disposing in the trash.

7. The last thing is to carefully remove your gloves and put them into a plastic bag.

Finally, instruct the client to carefully watch the injured area and to seek medical attention if the area becomes red, inflamed, or painful because these could be signs of a potentially serious infection, that if not promptly treated could worsen.

## 37:1 The client had a skin reaction after the product was removed. Could it be the actual UV gel is breaking down and that is what the client is reacting too instead of the remover?

Yes I agree, this is reaction is NOT caused by acetone. How can I say this so assuredly? Contrary to what some may believe acetone does not cause skin allergies and clients don't become allergic to acetone. Acetone can dry the skin and may cause skin irritation, but that's much different from an allergic reaction. Salt can dry and irritate skin as well, but your body doesn't become allergic to salt either. This skin reaction is most likely caused by uncured monomers or oligomers being released into the solvent when the nail coating breaks apart. Some nail professionals only cure their UV gel nails to 70% or less, which leaves a lot of unreacted ingredients inside the hardened nail enhancement. The same is true for UV gel polishes.

When any nail coating is NOT properly cured, the solvent may dissolve uncured ingredients and then may help let these same ingredients slip past the skin's outer surface barrier. Once inside the skin, certain specific substances can confuse the immune system and cause it to create an allergic skin reaction. But the solvent isn't the problem, the dissolved substances which are called the "solute", are what causes the allergy or skin irritation. That is why allergic skin reactions are much more likely to occur when the nail coatings are not properly cured, and are much less likely when nail coatings are properly cured. So, the first thing I would do is focus on ensuring proper cure. Ask yourself, is the correct nail lamp being used and as used directed? Are the UV bulbs cleaned and replaced regularly? Is the product being too thickly applied? Are the directions for use being followed and all instructions and warnings being heeded?

## 38:1 Why do adverse skin reactions happen, who is most susceptible and how can these reactions be prevented?

Adverse skin reactions occur in every area of the professional salon industry. Nail, skin and hair services can all cause problems for sensitive clients and for beauty professionals themselves. When it comes to nail salons, the vast majority of adverse skin reactions can be easily avoided, if you understand how. Adverse skin reactions come in two varieties; irritation and allergy. When something irritates the skin reddening, inflammation and itching are often the result. When the irritating substance is eliminated or removed, the skin returns to normal and the irritation heals. Allergies are very different. One main difference is that irritations go away once the irritant is removed.

Allergies last a lifetime; they never go away. Their symptoms can worsen over time or may seem to subside, but they can be triggered again at any time, sometimes even with the slightest skin exposure. The medical term for a skin allergy is "allergic contact dermatitis". These types of skin allergies account for approximately 80% of all cosmetic related skin problems. It is very important to understand that people don't become allergic to cosmetic products; they become allergic to certain cosmetic ingredients. Usually fragrances or preservatives are the culprits. These types of ingredients are beneficial for the vast majority of people and most of them will never experience any problems. However, a small number of people may develop skin allergies when significant skin over exposure occurs. Any substance or ingredient that causes skin allergies is called an "allergen". In other words, allergens are substances, which upon exposure can cause an allergy. It is a common myth that just about any substance can cause allergies. This is completely false. Only certain substances can cause allergic reactions. Water or acetone for instance do not cause skin allergies. Excessive exposure to either of these may cause irritation, but neither is capable of triggering allergic reactions. Not everyone is allergic to a specific allergen; that often depends on that individual's immune system.

The second important point to understand is that allergies to cosmetic products do not suddenly develop. Symptoms may take months or even years of repeated skin contact before they will appear. The process of developing an allergy to a particular substance is called "sensitization". For this reason, allergens are often referred to as sensitizers. The substance causing the allergy is usually called either a sensitizer or an allergen. Tree pollen is a common allergen, and so are cat hair, dust mites, bee stings, molds, nickel, and latex. What else do these all have in common? They are all naturally occurring substances. That's not a coincidence!

Most allergies are caused by naturally occurring substances. Our immune system is designed to protect us from nature. Nature is not the La-La land that many mistakenly believe it is. Nature is a dangerous place filled with all types of naturally occurring and potentially harmful substances. Our immune system is designed to protect us from naturally occurring dangers such as viruses and bacteria. It is a common myth that allergic reactions are caused by synthetic substances. The facts are, when a synthetic substance triggers an allergic reaction, it happens because the immune system was fooled into thinking the offending substance was natural. The immune system has no way to distinguish between natural and synthetic substances. Problems occur when the body mistakes synthetic substances for natural substances that are potentially harmful. The immune system sometimes overreacts to a harmless synthetic substance when they are mistaken for a potentially dangerous natural substance.

The immune system is like an army that never forgets. It's a massive fighting force that has the ability to wage a full-scale war against any foreign aggressor. Like any army, the immune system army has privates and generals, spies and assassins, sentries and scouts. Certain parts of the immune system act as spies- roaming the body and constantly on the lookout for potentially dangerous invaders. The immune system spies memorize details about the attacker and describe it in detailed messages they send back to the "generals". These spies even bring back prisoners for inspection. The "generals" then send messengers to alert the immune system army of a possible invasion and provide a description of the invading substance so the army can be on the lookout. Once the substance is under control and the threat is eliminated, the immune system strengthens its defenses and patiently waits for the next attack. When or if another attack comes, the immune system will be ready and prepared. In medical terms, this is called an "immune response".

The body has two separate immune systems, one that protects the inside of our bodies, and we have a second immune system in our skin that protects us from the outside world. Let's look at some examples so that we can better understand irritants and allergens and avoid their potential to harm the skin. Cleansing agents used in shampoos or hand and body washes contain ingredients that remove oil from the skin. These types of ingredients are called "surfactants". Washing the hands too often can remove excessive amounts of surface oils and give the skin a whitish appearance and will eventually cause the skin surface to flake or peel. The hands may even become red and inflamed, which are additional signs of skin irritation. In this case, if the hands are washed less often then they would not be so irritated and the appearance of the skin would improve. Usually, irritations will quickly reverse themselves when exposure to the irritating substances ceases. Surfactants can be irritants for some people.

As mentioned before, water can also be an irritant. When hands are always wet, they can become irritated. Interesting, some claim that constant water exposure dried out their skin, which of course makes no sense. Water makes things wet, not dry. This goes to show how many people don't pay attention to the words they use and this just adds to the confusion. This also makes it more difficult for them to find a viable solution, if they don't understand what the source of their problem is. Skin allergies cause many of the same symptoms as irritation. Irritation *and* allergies can both cause skin redness, swelling, itching, tiny blisters, even nail onycholysis and painful growths of pterygium under the free edge of the nail. The symptoms may appear similar, but the difference is that once you become allergic to a substance, you will be allergic to it for life. Your skin's immune system will always remember that it is allergic to that particular substance and will rapidly react when direct skin exposure occurs. We don't become allergic to vapors, instead only via direct prolonged and/or repeated contact with specific liquids or solid substances.

Only very potent allergic sensitizers such as certain poisonous plants can trigger immune responses after just a few exposures. Potent allergens are not used in salon products, in fact, they are carefully avoided by those who manufacture and supply cosmetic ingredients. Some ingredients (monomers and oligomers) used in nail enhancement products can be weak sensitizers for some individuals. This means that these ingredients are unlikely to cause allergic reactions under normal conditions of use; even so, prolonged and/or repeated skin contact with these products can cause some sensitive people to become allergic. I keep mentioning this because "prolonged and/or repeated contact" is the number one cause for allergic reactions to nail enhancements. Prolonged contact happens when some ingredients are allowed to sit on the skin for long periods of time, for example, sticky UV gels on the skin all day long would be considered prolonged contact.

Repeated contact occurs when the same area of skin is touched many times with the nail coating product. An example of this is a contaminated nail brush handle that is held between the same fingers, day after day or a contaminated table towel exposing the arm to monomer or UV gel or dusts or filings of improperly cured UV gel products, or using bare fingers to pick at the hairs on the UV gel or monomer liquid application brush, or repeated touching the sticky inhibition layer that sometimes forms on certain UV gels. Artificial nail coating products do not cause clients to become allergic after a single exposure. Sensitization to nail coatings typically takes four to six months or even years of direct skin exposure. One of the best ways to avoid skin allergies is to avoid prolonged and repeated skin contact.

Certain client's skin may be more sensitive than others. For example, pale skin is usually more sensitive to allergens than darker pigmented skin. Some clients or nail technicians may be overexposed for many years before eventually becoming allergic, while others develop initial symptoms after just a few months. Usually, symptoms will worsen with each continued exposure. Eventually, even the slightest contact with the allergen can trigger a major outbreak of visible symptoms. Determining the cause of the allergic reaction can be tricky. Unlike irritant contact dermatitis, the symptoms are not always restricted to the contact area. Sometimes, swelling and other signs may occur far from the point of contact, i.e. face, eyelids, armpits and glands in the throat or groin. In rare instances, some people develop hives (aka welts). Hives can appear on the wrist, arms, face or neck and are usually caused by direct skin exposure to the dusts from improperly cured nail coatings. Important reasons for why products must be properly cured and dusts in the salon should be cleaned up and not allowed to accumulate. Hives are smooth, slightly elevated areas on the skin. The area is either redder or paler than the surrounding skin and is often accompanied by severe itching. Hives may change size or shape or even disappear within a few hours.

Many other things are much more likely to cause hives, i.e. foods, medications, plants, clothing, etc. Do not automatically assume hives are related to cosmetic ingredient sensitivity. Typically, allergic contact symptoms are restricted to the site of skin contact and that should be your first clue. Look for what repeatedly contacted the site of the reaction over the past several months or years. Most are surprised to learn that an allergic reaction usually appears after several months or years of exposure. This can fool nail technicians into believing that the cause was something new or recent, i.e. a new polish or lotion. They don't realize it's probably something they've been using or doing for a long time.

Fortunately, tracking down the source of an allergy becomes a lot easier if you know what to look for. The first symptoms noticed are a temporary reddening or warming sensation that occurs directly at the site of contact. If overexposure continues the skin may appear dry, tight, flaky or itchy. In later stages, tiny water blisters or raised, red bumps are often seen around the proximal nail fold or at the fingertip. There may appear to be an overgrowth of tissue underneath the free edge. When overexposure continues these symptoms will worsen. Water blisters may develop into open sores, the fingertips may become cracked, and feel numb or an annoying itch may develop underneath the nail plate.

The nail technician's wrist or arm may also develop similar symptoms if the arm is repeatedly exposed to monomer, UV gel or improperly cured dusts. When this occurs, it would be wise to discontinue use of the product and to immediately change work practices to eliminate the over exposure to the skin. All artificial nail enhancement products, including UV gels, gel manicures, wraps, adhesives and monomer/polymer systems can cause allergic reactions in sensitive individuals, but none of them need cause problems. Adverse skin reactions are completely avoidable. By ensuring that uncured OR improperly cured nail coating and adhesive products don't contact any living skin, including your own. Each skin exposure increases the potential risk for irritation or allergy. Since at first there are no obvious negative effects when skin exposure happens, many nail technicians don't realize they risks they are taking. This is one reason why it is extremely important that you always leave a small margin between the product application and the client's skin. Responsible and safe nail professionals will never intentionally touch any nail enhancement product to the skin.

Other important tips to remember in order to avoid adverse skin reactions are: monomer liquids should only be used with the correct polymer powder, which is the one designed specifically for use with that particular monomer liquid. There is no such thing as a universal powder that works with any monomer liquid or vice versa. Also, using too much monomer liquid and not enough powder can create dusts or filings that are only partially cured and will increase the risks of allergic reactions. Beads should be of a medium consistency, never wet, since this can lead to under-curing. Using an overly large brush can cause skin over exposure to clients, so avoid using them. Large brushes also hold too much liquid monomer and this can lead to enhancements that contain too much monomer, which makes the dusts and filings more likely to cause an adverse skin reaction.

All UV cured nail coatings must be properly cured using the correct UV nail lamp by exposing the nail coating for the proper length of time. If not done, adverse skin reactions become more likely. The correct lamp is the one specified by the UV gel manufacturer. If no lamp is specified, I'd recommend finding and using a system that provides users with this information. Always remember, it's easy to avoid adverse skin reactions, if you take the proper steps to protect yourself and clients.

# Special Topics

## *Topic 1*

## The Complexity of Curing UV Nail Gels

I've noticed that many nail technicians tend to over simplify the UV curing process for nail coatings and this has created misunderstanding. In my opinion, UV cured nail coatings are the most technically sophisticated and complex products in the beauty industry. Many underestimate the various aspects of UV curing, including the nail lamps. They don't appreciate how many factors influence cure and instead over simplify everything, including "wattage", which is not as important as most believe. In fact, if you buy a lamp just because of its wattage, you are likely to be disappointed.

There are three types of cure for UV nail coatings: under-cure, over-cure and proper cure. Here is some information that you need to know to achieve "proper cure" and avoid the other possibilities. Curing is NOT about the wattage. Don't be fooled by those who just want to sell you a nail lamp. Wattage is "power consumption" and not "UV output". The second mistake that some make is to focus on the range of wavelengths emitted by their UV bulbs, however that is not enough and is only another part of all that must be considered to ensure a UV gel properly cures.

### What's Needed for Proper UV Curing?

In my scientific opinion, the best way is ensure a proper cure is to consistently apply a thin layer of UV gel with the correct thickness and then cure that thin layer for the proper length of time, using a nail lamp that emits the correct UV wavelengths needed to efficiently activate the photointiators in the UV gel. ALSO, those wavelengths can have neither too high nor too low of an intensity for the UV curing product. Too high of an intensity causes over-curing; too low of an intensity causes under-curing.

Besides the wavelength and intensity, even the DESIGN of the lamp is very important. For instance, the distance between the nail plates and the bulbs makes a very big difference in curing. Very small changes in this distance can have big consequences on curing. Most people don't think about the electronics inside the lamp. The electronic components drive the bulbs to create UV. These components influence UV intensity and different lamps have different components. If the exact same UV bulbs are used in two different brands of UV nail lamp, the bulbs can produce widely different UV intensities. It's important to note that old UV bulbs should be replaced with the same type and model of UV bulb. Fluorescent style bulbs should generally be changed 2-4 times per year depending on how often the nail lamps are used.

Too few understand how important the design of the nail lamp is in curing. The positioning of the bulbs and even type of interior reflector material used are VERY important factors that influence curing. This is why it is wrong to assume that only wattage is important, when it is the least important of these factors. The most confusing of all, is that many are fooled when the UV products harden. They incorrectly assume that hardening means properly cured, but in many cases it is not. UV nail coatings will harden when they cure more than 50%. However, to obtain the best properties and avoid causing skin sensitivities, these coatings should be cured to around 90%. So, there are many clients walking around with under cured enhancements, which are more prone to service breakdown and more likely to cause adverse skin reactions, especially for the nail technicians who are repeatedly exposed to partially cured UV gel dust and filings.

How do I know this information is correct? I have spent many years developing some of the leading UV nail products in the world and am also one of the top scientific experts on UV nail lamps. These are the facts as I know them. This information is important because too many nail professionals don't realize that many of their service breakdown problems are probably due to improper cure. Improper cure can cause everything from cracking, breaking, shattering, lifting, pitting, discoloration, bubbles, and onycholysis to adverse skin reactions. In my opinion, improper curing is a leading cause of skin sensitivity, producing symptoms such as skin redness, itching, water blisters, etc. These are completely avoidable and would not happen if these coatings were properly applied and cured. In short, don't use a UV nail lamp (either LED or fluorescent style) unless it is recommended by the UV curing product manufacturers and then always cure these products exactly as directed.


## Topic 2

## Risks of Improperly Curing Nail Coatings

Recently, I recommended to a group of nail professionals that they should NOT try every new nail product that comes along, especially if it is a UV cure nail coating product. Nail professionals are better off focusing on only a few different systems, (or even just one) and specializing in the proper and correct use of that system(s); including the proper use of the UV nail lamp unit that is specifically designed to cure their system(s) of choice. Many nail technicians want to use any nail lamp unit to cure any UV gel they use and wonder what's the harm in that?

Improper curing of a nail coating becomes more likely when the incorrect nail lamp unit is used. When nail coatings are improperly cured, the risk of allergic sensitivity for both the nail professional and her clients increases. I've spent more than 20 years researching why some nail technicians and clients develop adverse skin reactions, while others using the same products do not develop such issues. My research has identified several key factors that can increase the potential for developing adverse skin reactions and I talk about these factors in my book, "Nail Structure and Product Chemistry" 2nd Edition, and many articles which are available at DougSchoon.com. There are many non-product related articles and webinars on my website that explain how and why adverse skin reactions occur, as well as how to avoid them.

Adverse skin reactions to nail products often seem to just "appear", but in actuality they take time to develop, usually months, sometimes years. They are almost always a result of prolonged and/or repeated skin contact. This helps explain why prolonged or repeated skin contact with improperly cured UV gel products is a leading cause for adverse skin reactions for nail technicians.

Daily contact with filings/dusts from under cured nail coatings can lead to either skin irritation or allergic skin reactions. The risks are real! But it is important to know that these risks can be increased or greatly decreased; depending upon the choices the nail technician makes about product application, curing and removal. Fortunately, adverse skin reactions are easy to avoid. One way is by ensuring the nail coatings are properly cured on a consistent basis. This is accomplished by using the proper procedures and/or equipment needed to prevent "under curing". Just because a product hardens, doesn't mean it is properly cured. Artificial nail coatings will harden when they are only 50% cured. This means a nail coating might be only halfway cured and the nail technician may mistakenly believe it is fully and properly cured.

Just as under curing can be related to skin sensitivies, over-curing of products often causes discoloration, service breakdown and even onycholysis (nail plate separation from the nail bed). Difficult or forceful removal of a nail coating often leads to natural nail surface damage. The surface white spots associated with UV gel manicures are almost always caused by improper removal of a nail coating, which is even more likely to occur when nail coating products are over-cured, since over-curing can make them more difficult to remove. Onycholysis may occur when any type of nail coating becomes over heated and burns the sensitive tissue of the nail bed. This can happen when using LED-style UV nail lamps to cure nail coating products designed to cure with traditional-style UV nail lamps. Ouch!

Along with using the right lamp with the right UV gel system as directed by the manufacturer, it is also important to understand and heed all warnings on the package label and Safety Data Sheets (aka MSDS). For instance, products that are designed to be part of a "system", should be used as a system and not mixed and matched with products not intended to be a part of the "system". The same is true for all liquid/powder systems. You must properly use the monomer liquid of your choice with the correct polymer powder and at the proper ratio of liquid to powder. Nail technicians should NOT make up their own powder blends or alter the ratios if they expect the product to properly and safely perform. There is no such thing as a "universal liquid" or powder that works with "any liquid" nor is there a nail lamp that works with all UV gels, not when proper curing and safety is the goal! There are plenty of people out there who just want to sell their UV nail lamps (or powders) and will often tell nail technicians things that have no basis in facts. My advice is to save your money and invest in the correct nail lamp that was specifically designed for the system(s) of your choice. Don't buy a product unless you intend to properly cure it. Ensuring proper cure is one of a nail professional's most important responsibilities. If you would like more information on how to properly cure nail products, please check out the articles my website, DougSchoon.com. Happy Curing!

## Topic 3

## Can UV Nails Be Over Cured?

Yes they can, but over-curing is avoidable. It happens in two ways: 1) too much UV energy is used or 2) the nail coating is exposed to significant levels of UV after leaving the salon. In other words, UV nail coatings can be over cured in the short-term and/or long-term.

## Too Much UV Energy

When a nail coating is exposed to too much UV energy, it will cure too quickly. This can lead to service breakdown, nail damage and even nail infections. How? All UV nail coatings release small amounts of heat when they cure. This is why some clients feel a slight warming. When over cured, the same UV gel coating may become very hot, resulting in a painful nail bed burning sensation.

For example, a layer of nail coating designed to be properly cured for two minutes under a fluorescent-style UV nail lamp can heat up quickly when cured under a LED-style UV nail lamp, heating the nail bed in excess of 120oF (48oC), which can result in painful burns that may lead to nail plate separation (onycholysis). Onycholysis allows bacteria easy access the nail bed, making infections easier to occur. Over-curing can make nail coatings more difficult to remove, which can lead to nail damage. Why? Surface white spots often occur when products are scraped from the nail plate with too much force. When nail coatings are more difficult to remove, scraping damage is more likely.

## UV Exposure After the Service

UV gel nail coatings can also be affected by tanning beds and natural sunlight. Poorly formulated or incorrectly manufactured nail coating products are more likely to be brittle, discolor, crack, break or lift (i.e. excessive free edge chipping) and it's often due to continued UV exposure. Certain ingredients used in lower quality nail coatings can turn dark brown or become yellow with continued UV exposure. Long term UV exposure can cause some nail coatings to lose their flexibility and become more brittle, Do It Right- Never Accept Substitutes!

How can nail technicians avoid over -curing nail coatings? One of the best ways is to always use the UV nail lamp specifically designed for the UV nail coating product of your choice. Follow manufacturer's instructions and heed all warnings.

Properly maintaining the UV nail lamp is of great importance. Replaceable UV bulbs must be changed on a regular basis to ensure proper curing. Heavily used UV nail lamps may need bulb replacement every three months; moderate use may require bulb replacement twice per year. It is VERY important to use the replacement bulbs supplied by the UV gel product/lamp manufacturer. NEVER substitute for another UV bulb type or brand. Incorrect bulb use results in improper curing and potential hazard to the client's skin as some bulbs are NOT intended for use with UV nail lamps.

High quality UV bulbs may cost more, but in the long run trying to save money by buying less expensive bulbs is likely to cost far more than it saves.

To learn more about properly curing UV nail coatings, check out my free webinar on this subject: http://vimeo.com/51532960

## Topic 4

### Pregnancy and Artificial Nail Coatings

When your clients discover they're pregnant, one of the first questions they will ask nail professionals is, "Can I keep wearing my nail enhancements during my pregnancy?" The answer is YES; they can safely wear artificial nails! There is no reason to believe wearing artificial nail enhancements or polish during pregnancy is harmful. All artificial nail coatings polymerize and harden within three minutes. This eliminates the chance of any product penetrating beyond the very topmost layers of the nail plate. The ingredients used to make nail coatings are used widely around the world in thousands of different applications and are among the most widely studied ingredients in the world. The ingredients are NOT considered to create risks during pregnancy.

What about pregnant nail technicians? Is it safe for them to work in a salon? Of course they can! Pregnant nail technicians that aren't already working safely will need to make changes in their work routines and pay close attention to the rules of working safely, but this is true regardless of your occupation. A well-informed physician will usually advise mothers-to-be to avoid alcohol and tobacco, as studies indicate these may cause abnormal fetal development. Fortunately, scientific studies indicate there are no such risks with artificial nail products. To put things in their proper perspective; smoking is many thousands of times more dangerous than any nail salon service.

Here are ten tips that can help you work safer:

1.  Use products properly, always precisely follow directions and heed all warnings.

2.  Properly dispose of trash; use a trash can with a self-closing lid and empty it often throughout the day.

3.  Avoid skin contact with UV curing gels, monomer liquids, adhesives (glues), resins and primers, etc.

4.  Wearing disposable nitrile gloves is one great way to minimize the potential for skin contact.

5.  Wash hands often; always before servicing any client, eating or touching the face.

6.  Keep products tightly closed and use covers on dampen dishes to minimize evaporation.

7.  Wear a well-fitted dust mask, preferably one rated as N-95 or equivalent, especially if you use an electric file. Drill oils should also be used to control dusts. Avoid doctor or surgical masks since they aren't designed for use with dusts.

8.  Make sure your salon ventilation system is working properly, has been recently cleaned and is supplying an adequate amount of fresh air. Contact a local HVAC company for guidance. Use a "source capture" ventilation system to improve air quality if the salon ventilation is not adequate.

9. Obtain the SDS (aka MSDS) for all of your products and review them with your doctor.

10. Talk to your doctor if you are experiencing any work-related symptoms, e.g. weakness, light-headedness or difficulty breathing etc.

Working safely is easy to do, so pay attention to these recommendations even if you aren't planning on becoming pregnant. Working safely is the responsibility of every salon professional!

## Topic 5

## Mixing Products:
## What's the Harm in Doing That?

Nail Professionals work in a unique and diverse profession and often unintentionally put themselves and their clients at risk. They regularly work with the most technologically advanced products in the beauty industry. Many nail coatings are based on high-tech substances used to create everything from bone cements to dental implants or contact lenses to bullet proof glass. Nail Professionals also work with finger nails and toe nails that may become diseased or injured. When faced with medical conditions of the hands and feet, some clients expect their Nail Professional to diagnosis and treat or prescribe a treatment for their condition, even though this is inappropriate and should only be done by a qualified medical professional. When you add to this the fact that many Nail Professionals love to "experiment" and try new things, it becomes easy to see how problems can occur, especially when manufacturer's instructions are ignored and nail products are used in a manner they were not intended to be used.

## What's the Harm?

Without a deep understanding of chemistry or medicine, this could create significant problems for clients, Nail Professionals and salons. Here are a few examples. Many products are intended to be used together as a "system" and in very specific ways to ensure safe use and to achieve the intended final result. Monomer liquids are designed to be used with specific powders. Using the wrong powder or using the incorrect ratio of liquid to powder (too wet) can lead to skin irritation, allergy or even "onycholysis", a condition where the nail plate detaches from the nail bed. Each of these same issues can occur when the incorrect nail lamp is used to cure a UV gel. Improper use of salon disinfectants can lead to infections that may result in injury or a lawsuit that could jeopardize a Salon Professional or salon's livelihood.

What's my point? When products are improperly mixed or used contrary to directions/instructions, there may be unintended consequences that could cause harm to clients and/or Nail Professionals. Contrary to what some believe, Nail Professionals should NOT use professional products in any fashion they choose. Instead, manufacturer's instructions should ALWAYS be carefully followed and all warnings heeded. If a Nail Professional disagrees with, or wishes to alter the directions, or doesn't understand the instructions, then they would be wise to contact the product manufacturer for guidance before proceeding.

I greatly admire the curious, inquisitive nature of Nail Professionals who like to "experiment" with their products and realize that it is their ingenuity and creativity that drives them to do this! These are great qualities that anyone can benefit from, IF properly channeled. But, when "experimenting" means disregarding the manufacturer's directions or warnings, then this is inappropriate and should not be done. Instead, a Nail Professional's curiosity would be better directed towards:

a) Learning more about the structure of the natural nail and surrounding skin and how each functions AND

b) Gaining a better understanding about how and why nail products work.

Those who gain a deeper understanding in these areas are much less likely to misuse nail products or encounter any of the problems described above. Avoid focusing solely on how to skillfully apply these products; that's only half the picture! Gone forever are the days when product application and removal was all that mattered. Nail Professionals need to understand how their professional products work and why they work the way they do. That's what my website is dedicated to teaching, so please check it out by visiting DougSchoon.com. It's free, interesting and easy to understand. Best of all... it's just a mouse click away. I hope you enjoy!

## *Topic 6*

### Myth 1: Nails Need to Breath.

No, they don't! There is no reason to believe that nails need to "breathe". Nails aren't alive and don't have lungs nor do they have any ability to absorb air into the nail plate. This myth makes no sense on many levels! In short, nails do NOT require an external air supply and do not breathe or exhale. 100% of the oxygen needed by the nail matrix to create a new nail plate comes from the blood stream and 0% comes from the outside world.

Everything the nail plate needs to properly grow and function is delivered and/or removed by the blood flow to the matrix area and nail bed. The matrix is where the nail plate is created from nutrients which can ONLY be delivered by the blood stream. Neither "air" nor "nutrients" can be absorbed or "fed" to the nail plate from any external source.

Moisture and natural nail oils leave the nail bed and pass through the nail plate at slower than normal rates, however they aren't "trapped". The nail plate's moisture content is increased by 10-15%, and the oil content increases only slightly; both serve to increase the flexibility of the natural nail plate.

Waste products are removed from the matrix area and surrounding tissues by the blood as well, and are not released into the nail plate. Normal, healthy nail plates would continue to grow and thrive in a completely air-free environment, as long as a healthy flow of blood to the nail is maintained, so clearly... nails don't need to breathe!

## Myth 2: Nails need to take a break from enhancements.

Not true! Nothing is gained by removing artificial nail enhancements or coatings for a few weeks or months before reapplying them. Since the nails do not need to "breathe", no benefit is gained by waiting to reapply artificial nail enhancements or coatings, which includes nail polish. Nor does it make sense to assume the nails only need to breathe "every once-in-a-while". This faulty reasoning is not supported by the facts.

However as a general rule if the nail plate or surrounding skin shows signs of moderate to serious damage, injury, infection or adverse skin reactions, nail enhancements should be not be applied. Why? In most countries, including the US, nail technicians are only permitted to provide cosmetic services on healthy skin and nails. Unhealthy nail conditions are "medical conditions" which should be examined by a doctor (or podiatrist) who can provide a proper diagnosis and treatment, if required. Nail technicians are not licensed to practice medicine. In cases of adverse skin reactions, discontinue use until the client's doctor can be consulted as to the actual causes and possible solutions.

## Myth 3: UV gels are better for your nails than acrylics.

Absolutely false! Every type of UV gel nails and all types of so-called "acrylic" (aka liquid/powder) nail enhancements are made from acrylic ingredients and are cured by acrylic chemistry, therefore both of these types of nail enhancement coatings are just as "acrylic" as the other, regardless of how they are marketed. Other than marketing claims and application procedures, the only real differences between these two types of systems are in the way they harden (polymerize).

UV gels utilize a UV sensitive curing agent to harden the nail coating, while liquid/powder systems use heat sensitive curing agents to achieve the same end result. A UV sensitive curing agent could be placed into a liquid/powder system and cured via UV nail lamps and the reverse is also true; a heat sensitive curing agent could be placed into a UV gel and these could be cured without UV. Of course, neither of these makes sense for salon products, which is why this isn't done, but the point remains... these two types of systems are very similar and one is NOT any better for the nail or safer than the other. This is because "both" UV gels and liquid/powder systems are safe when used per manufacturer instructions and "neither" will harm the natural nail when properly applied, maintained and removed by trained professionals.

Remember, wearing any type of enhancement or coating can lead to nail damage IF the nail technician improperly applies the nail coating or if they (or their clients) improperly remove them. Nail enhancement and other nail coating products are safe for the natural nail if properly applied, maintained and removed. No type of artificial nail is safer or better for the natural nail than another. If nail damage occurs while wearing enhancements, this is usually a result of over-filing or other improper application or removal procedures. To prevent this, nail professionals should educate themselves about how to work in a manner that protects the natural nail from damage.

## Myth 4: Nail coatings are bad for the nails.

This is NOT correct. Nail coatings don't harm the nail plate and any nail damage is usually a result of improper application and/or removal. If the nail plate underneath the enhancement is much thinner than the area of new nail growth, this strongly indicates excessive filing with a manual or electric file. Overly aggressive filing causes the majority of nail plate damage seen in salons. This isn't done just in discount salons, it happens even in high end salons and is indicative of an improperly trained nail professional.

If upon removal the plates are not any thinner, but feel like they are overly flexible, this does NOT indicate the nails are "weaker". Instead, this is a temporary effect created by an increased moisture content of the nail plate. Nail coatings increase the moisture content of the plate by 10-15% and this can last up to 12-24 hours after coating removal; after which the moisture content returns to normal, as will the nail plate's normal level of rigidity.

When the nail surface is covered with dry looking white patches, this is usually due to improper removal, e.g. scraping or peeling nail coatings from the nail plate. Soaking the natural nail for even a few minutes in acetone or water will temporarily soften the surface making it temporarily more susceptible to damage from wooden or metal implements that pry, push or force the remaining residual nail coatings from the nail plate. Instead, a good rule to follow is, "Use the utmost care for 60 minutes after immersing natural nails in any liquid for more than 60 seconds."

Other damage, e.g. onycholysis, is also usually caused by improper filing or removal techniques

Infections do occur, but they are relatively uncommon and can be easily avoided by practicing proper cleaning and disinfection. The facts are, when artificial enhancements or coatings are carefully and properly applied, maintained, and removed by a trained, skilled, and knowledgeable nail professional- they will not cause nail damage! The vast majority of damaged nail plates are caused by improper use- over filing and/or scraping the nail plate to remove products or by client nail abuse, e.g. picking or prying off nail coatings.

## Myth 5: Medications cause artificial nails to lose adhesion and lift.

In general, taking a medication for a month or two isn't going to affect adhesion of artificial nails or coatings to the nail plates. The same is true for birth control or other over-the-counter (OTC) medications. These aren't likely to adversely affect the nail plate either. Generally when people are taking medications over a long term, it is because their body isn't functioning normally. It is more likely that their illness is what's affecting the nails, not the medication. The health of the natural nail is often a window into the health of the individual. Chemotherapy is often given for long periods of time and is an example of medications that can adversely affect the natural nail and may contribute to adhesion loss. OTC medicines and other types of medications taken for short periods (e.g. antibiotics) are unlikely to cause adhesion loss.

Anesthetic given during surgery is sometimes blamed for nail problems. Since many people are leery of medication of any type, they jump to this conclusion quickly. Even so, it is FAR more likely that nail growth would be affected by the accident/illness and/or the fact the body is in recovery from surgery.

In short, nail techs should NOT suspect medications until all other potential sources of the problem have been investigated and ruled out. Medications are RARELY the cause of artificial nail adhesion loss. Keep in mind that these problems may also be caused by something the client is doing, e.g. a sudden lifestyle change.

## Myth 6: Vitamins and nutrients absorb into the nail to make them stronger and healthier.

As described above, vitamins or nutrients can NOT be fed to the nail plate externally and in many countries it is not legal to make such claims. Vitamins and/or nutrients only make nail plates stronger or healthier when they are ingested in foods and delivered to the nail via the blood stream. In the US and other places, it is against the law for a cosmetic to claim to provide nutritional benefits or value. Only foods can provide nutrition to the body, not cosmetics!

To be clear, some nail oils use "vitamin E", but its function is NOT for nutritional purposes or strengthening. The proper cosmetic label name for Vitamin E is "tocopherol". Tocopherol or one of its related derivatives (e.g. tocopherol acetate) is used as an antioxidant to help protect the nail plate keratin from damage caused by environmental exposure (e.g. cleaners, hand washing, gardening). As long as no nutritional benefits are claimed, this is an appropriate cosmetic claim since there is strong science to support Vitamin E's antioxidant abilities.

## Myth 7: Nail oil applied directly to a fresh nail enhancement will cause lifting.

This is false, when the enhancement is properly applied; if not properly applied then this can be true. When properly applied, artificial nail coatings form a tight seal with the nail plate, therefore nail oils cannot get underneath the coating to cause separation and lifting. The benefit of these natural oils is that they can penetrate into the surface of the nail enhancement to increase the nail coating's flexibility and durability. Penetrating nail oils should be applied daily, to keep the enhancement flexible, beautiful and to condition the surrounding living tissue. If the artificial nail enhancement was improperly applied, there may be small areas of pre-existing separation between the coating and the nail plate (delamination). When this occurs, nail oils may seep underneath the coating to cause lifting. Even so, there are clear and significant benefits to using nail oils on natural nails and artificial nail coatings. If their use leads to increased lifting of the enhancements, don't discontinue use of the nail oil. Instead, carefully reexamine your techniques and ensure you are performing careful and proper nail preparation, including nail surface cleansing and properly applying and curing the nail enhancement or coating products.

## Myth 8: MMA is dangerous and that is why it shouldn't be used to make artificial nails.

This is false! Methyl methacrylate monomer (MMA) is used all around the world for dental prosthetics, contact lenses, and is even implanted into the body as a bone cement, so the effect of exposure to humans is well understood. MMA is NOT considered to be a cancer causing agent nor does it damage unborn fetuses. These are myths! Even so, there are several reasons to avoid MMA monomer as a nail coating.

MMA nail products do not adhere well to the nail plate, so nail technicians must shred the surface of the nail plate with an abrasive, coarse grit file, causing thinning and weakening in order to ensure the enhancements adhere to the nail plate. Traditional products are designed to adhere to the natural nail plate without the need to over file the nail plate.

MMA creates the hardest and most rigid nail enhancements. So, they are very difficult to break. If jammed or caught, the overly filed and thinned natural nail plate is much more likely to break than the MMA enhancement. This can lead to serious nail damage and possible subsequent bacterial infection.

MMA enhancements are extremely difficult to remove, because of the filing techniques used to make them adhere and because they don't easily dissolve in product removers. Therefore, MMA enhancements are usually pried from the nail plate, creating still more damage to the overly thinned nail plate.

The information above applies ONLY to MMA monomer. Powders containing MMA should really be called PMMA (poly methyl methacrylate). PMMA has completely different chemical structure/properties and is considered safe for use in artificial nails. PMMA in a sheet form is called Plexiglas™ and Lucite™.

## Myth 9: You should wear a mask when you do nails.

False, if you are working with a source capture ventilation system (SCV); you don't want or need to use a face mask. Even a high quality, properly fitting N-95 dust mask won't work as well as a source capture ventilation system. Why? When properly fitted, an N-95 dust mask WILL protect against inhalation of tiny airborne dust particles, but NOT vapors. SCV systems prevent exposure by collecting both dusts and vapors- keeping both out of the nail technician's breathing zone and salon air.

When properly maintained with the carbon filters changed regularly, SCV systems are a great way to help ensure salon air quality remains safe and everyone is breathing comfortably during working hours. Several dust collecting systems are great too and in general, I do recommend their use in salons. Even so, dust collection systems should be used in conjunction with another ventilation system which lowers exposure to vapors. Both dusts and vapors must be properly controlled. SVC systems do both, which is why I fully support their use in salons.

## Myth 10: Nail technicians don't need to learn about the science behind natural and artificial nails.

What? That's ridiculous; the biggest myth of them all! The best artists know their paints and canvas, just as sculptors know their chisels and stones and a master woodworker could tell you all the intricacies of wood. Wouldn't it benefit any nail technicians to have a deeper understanding of the natural nail and nail products? Understanding both the anatomy and microscopic structure of the nail plate is necessary for anyone who provides nail services. Imagine the nails you could do if you understood the science behind nail products and how they all work? You can.

# Acknowledgements

*Technical Editor:*

**Holly L Schippers**
FingerNailFixer®
http://fingernailfixer.com
http://youtube.com/fingernailfixer
http://nailsmag.com/fingernailfixer


*Photographer:*

**Paul Rollins**
http://paulrollinsphotography.com/


*Back Cover Photograph:*

**Judy Landis-Storm**

# Link Index

**Nail Manufacturer's Council on Safety (NMC)**
https://probeauty.org/nmc/

**Guidelines for Controlling and Minimizing Inhalation Exposure to Nail Products**
https://probeauty.org/docs/nmc/Inhalation.pdf

**US Center for Disease Control**
http://www.cdc.gov/

**Nail Structure and Product Chemistry 2nd Edition**
http://schoonscientific.com/purchase-books-dvd.html

**Reference Materials for Nail Professionals**
http://dougschoon.com

**Webinar on Properly Curing Nail Coatings**
http://vimeo.com/51532960

# Coming Soon

Doug Schoon Answers Questions about

Natural Nails: Products and Services

Volume II

Based on the Internet video series

"Face-to-Face with Doug Schoon"

Volume II

Natural Nail Structure

Natural Nail Service/Treatment

Pedicure and Foot Related

Ingredients

Storage/Disposal

Unusual Conditions

Special Topics

Printed in Great Britain
by Amazon